THE OFFICIAL
IPSWICH TOWN
QUIZ BOOK

1,000 Questions on The Tractor Boys

THE OFFICIAL IPSWICH TOWN QUIZ BOOK

1,000 Questions on The Tractor Boys

Compiled by Chris Cowlin

Forewords by John Wark and Jason Dozzell

APEX PUBLISHING LTD

First published in hardback in 2010 by

Apex Publishing Ltd
PO Box 7086, Clacton on Sea, Essex, CO15 5WN, England
www.apexpublishing.co.uk

British Library Cataloguing-in-Publication Data
A catalogue record for this book
is available from the British Library

ISBN: 1-906358-85-0   978-1-906358-85-3

Typeset in 10.5pt Chianti Bdlt Win95BT

Cover Design: Siobhan Smith

Printed in Great Britain by the
MPG Books Group, Bodmin and King's Lynn

Dedication:
To my children, Harry and Aimee - future football fans!

FOREWORD

It is a great honour to be asked to write the foreword to 'The Official Ipswich Town Quiz Book' compiled by Chris Cowlin.

I first signed for Ipswich as an apprentice when I was 16-years-old, then in 1975 Sir Bobby Robson gave me my debut in the clubs 3-2 FA Cup quarter-final win over Leeds United, I became a regular in the team during the 1976/1977 season.

The 1978 FA Cup win was the best highlight in my Ipswich career, the only disappointment is I hit the post twice in the game! To play in an FA Cup final at the age of 21 was fantastic and will always go down as one of my best football memories of my playing career.

1981 was a great year for me and Town, winning the UEFA Cup, finishing runners-up in the First Division and then winning the PFA Players' Player of the Year and Young European Player of the Year – what an achievement! Something I am very proud of.

I played with some great players at Portman Road including the FA Cup winning team and UEFA team. When I think back to when I played 65 games in a season, it was hard going, once scoring 36 goals as a midfielder, including 14 in Europe.

Ipswich Town Football club has played a massive part in my life, playing for them in the 70s, 80s and 90s, not a lot of people know this but I was actually going to retire when I returned to the club for a third spell from Middlesbrough in 1991, but when a few players got injured I stepped in during the 1991/1992 season, then ended up being the clubs Player of the Year and we won promotion to the Premier League – a great achievement, to be playing at the age of 39! I better not give you any more information of myself as I will make the John Wark section in the book very easy!

For the last 10 years I have been a host at Portman Road during match days, something I thoroughly enjoy, meeting new people and telling stories about my career. I still like to play a bit, playing in legends matches and charity games.

Now on to this great book, by buying this book you are helping the clubs Community Trust as the compiler, Chris Cowlin is raising money for them from each book sale. This quiz book is a fans dream, full of fascinating facts and figures covering virtually everything! It is also an excellent reference book for people wanting to learn about this great football club. I hope you enjoy this book as much as I did it certainly had me scratching my head!

Best wishes

John Wark

Ipswich Town Football Club, 1975-1984, 1988-1990 and 1991-1997

FOREWORD

I was delighted when I was contacted to write the foreword to
The Official Ipswich Town Quiz Book which has been compiled
by Chris Cowlin.

Ipswich Town Football Club holds a special place in my heart;
I first signed for the club and was signed on schoolboy terms
by the legendary manager, the late, great Sir Bobby Robson. I
made my club debut in February 1984, coming on a substitute
against Coventry City in a 3-1 win, a great memory for me
being only 16 years old, and I scored the second goal in the
game! At the time, I actually became the youngest ever player
to score in the First Division.

In the mid-1980s I became a regular in the Blues team and
was then selected for the England under-21 team, winning 9
caps.

During the 1988/1989 season I finished Town's joint top goal
scorer with Dalian Atkinson and John Wark, with 13 goals. I
was also glad to score 16 goals during our promotion season
during 1991/1992, which meant promotion to the Premier
League.

After playing for Ipswich for 10 seasons, I left Portman Road
for Spurs in August 1993, unfortunately various injuries
restricted the number of games I played for Tottenham.

It was nice to return to Portman Road for a second spell in
October 1997. In my Ipswich Town career I made over 400
appearances, scoring over 70 goals. I can honestly say that I
enjoyed every minute of it, playing alongside and against

some great players and under three good managers – Bobby Ferguson (who handed me by club debut), John Duncan and John Lyall.

So, to the book ... there is something for every fan in this book; Chris has just about covered all you would ever want to know about the club, including players, managers, opponents, transfers, kit, scores, fees, trophies, club honours and much more...

I know that Ipswich Town fans of all ages will be entertained for hours with questions about the Tractor Boys past and present. I hope you all enjoy this wonderful quiz book as much as I did - some great memories!

Best wishes
Jason Dozzell
Ipswich Town Football Club, 1983-1993 and 1997

INTRODUCTION

I would first of all like to thank John Walk and Jason Dozzell for writing the forewords to this book; they are both legends of Ipswich Town so I am very grateful for their help on this project.

I would also like to thank all the past players of Ipswich Town Football Club, and various newspapers and magazines for their comments and reviews on this book (these can be found at the back of the book). Thanks also goes to Malcolm Thompson and Anthony Grunberg.

I would also like to thank Terry Baxter at ITFC for his help and advice during the books compilation.

I am honoured to donate £1 from each book sale to the 'ITFC Charitable Trust'. The Trust is a company with Charitable Status aiming to provide high quality sports and education programmes to children, young people and adults from across the region. The Trust is a key department of Ipswich Town Football Club and they aim to achieve excellence in all they do. A very worthwhile cause!

I hope you enjoy this book. Hopefully it should bring back some wonderful memories!

In closing, I would like to thank all my friends and family for encouraging me to complete this book.

Chris Cowlin

Best wishes
Chris Cowlin

www.apexpublishing.co.uk

CLUB HISTORY

1. In which year was the club formed – 1877, 1878 or 1879?

2. True or false: Ipswich Town did not turn professional until 1936?

3. The club is known by which three nicknames?

4. Who was appointed as Ipswich Town manager in January 1969?

5. What did the club win in 1973 and 1975 and then again in 2005?

6. Which goalkeeper did Ipswich sign from Sampdoria during July 2001, costing a club record of £4.75 million?

7. Who were Ipswich playing when they achieved their club record League win of 7-0 during November 1964 in Division Two?

8. True or false: Ipswich Town became Champions of Division One at the first attempt in 1961/62, having been promoted from Division Two the previous season?

9. How many times have Ipswich Town won the FA Cup during their history?

10. In which year did Marcus Evans buy the club and become club chairman?

ROY KEANE

11. Which team did Roy manage between 2006 and 2008?

12. In which month during 2009 was Roy appointed as Town manager?

13. Against which Welsh club did Ipswich play in Roy's first game as Ipswich manager, winning 3-0 away from home?

14. From which club did Roy sign Lee Martin for The Blues during July 2009?

15. To what position in the League did Roy guide the club in his first full season in charge at Portman Road, during 2009/10?

16. What is Roy's middle name – Maurice, Martin or Malcolm?

17. For which country was Roy a full international during his playing days, winning 66 caps and scoring 9 goals?

18. For which team did Roy play between 1990 and 1993, before joining Manchester United?

19. How many Premier League winners' medals did Roy pick up whilst a Manchester United player – 5, 7 or 9?

20. Which midfielder did Roy sign for Ipswich Town during September 2009?

GEORGE BURLEY

21. In what position did George play during his playing days?

22. When George left Portman Road in 1985 which team did he join?

23. True or false: George won the FA Premier League Manager of the Month award for November 2000?

24. George was appointed manager of which country in January 2008, only to leave the position in November 2009 after 14 matches?

25. Who was George's assistant when he became Ipswich Town manager in 1994?

26. Can you name the two winners' medals that George won during his Ipswich Town playing career?

27. In which year was George born – 1954, 1955 or 1956?

28. Which Essex-based team did George manage prior to taking over as Town manager in 1994?

29. Against which team did George record his first win as Blues manager during January 1995, winning 4-1 at home in the Premier League?

30. To what position in the League did George guide Ipswich in his first full season in charge, 1995//96 – 5th, 6th or 7th?

PLAYER OF THE YEAR -1

Match up the season with the player who won the award

31.	2009/10	Shefki Kuqi
32.	2008/09	Ian Westlake
33.	2007/08	Mark Venus
34.	2006/07	Marcus Stewart
35.	2005/06	Gareth McAuley
36.	2004/05	Jonathan Walters
37.	2003/04	Richard Wright
38.	2002/03	Sylvain Legwinski
39.	2001/02	Fabian Wilnis
40.	2000/01	Matt Holland

BOBBY ROBSON

41. True or false: Bobby played for Ipswich during his playing career?

42. How many England international caps did Bobby win during his playing career, scoring 4 goals – 10, 20 or 30?

43. What was the first Cup that Bobby won as Town boss?

44. Which team did Bobby go on to manage for eight years when he left Portman Road in 1982?

45. Following on from the previous question, who took over as manager of The Blues when Bobby left?

46. In what year was a life-size statue of Bobby unveiled opposite the Cobbold Stand at Portman Road, in recognition of his achievements with the club?

47. To what position in Division One did Bobby guide Town in season 1978/79?

48. In what year was Bobby appointed as Blues manager?

49. Which team did Bobby manage between 1999 and 2004, the last managerial appointment of his career?

50. Which Dutch club did Bobby manage in the early 1990s and then again in the late 1990s?

RAY CRAWFORD

51. True or false: Ray holds the record for scoring the most League goals for Ipswich Town FC?

52. How many League goals did Ray score during his Ipswich Town career – 104, 154 or 204?

53. Ray was the first player to score five goals in a competitive match for Ipswich, in a game against which team during September 1962 in the European Cup?

54. Against which opponents did Ray score four goals in a League Cup 2nd round game during September 1967?

55. How many League hat-tricks did Ray score for Town during the 1960/61 season?

56. Against which team did Ray make his League debut in October 1958, scoring twice in a 4-2 away defeat?

57. In between his two playing spells at Portman Road Ray played for which two Midlands teams?

58. How many full England caps did Ray win whilst at Portman Road, scoring one goal for his country?

59. What is the name of Ray's autobiography, published in 2007?

60. How many League appearances did Ray make for Town during his playing days at Portman Road – 320, 322 or 324?

FA CUP WINNERS – 1978

61.   Where was the final played?

62.   Which London team did Ipswich beat in the final?

63.   Who scored Town's only goal in the 1-0 win?

64.   Following on from the previous question, in which minute was the goal scored – 66th, 77th or 88th?

65.   Which Ipswich player hit the woodwork twice during the final?

66.   Which winger came on as a substitute for Town during the 78th minute?

67.   Can you name 7 of the starting 11 that played for The Blues in the final?

68.   Who was Ipswich Town's captain, lifting the FA Cup for the first time in their history?

69.   Which team did Ipswich beat 3-1 in the FA Cup semi-final, played at Highbury?

70.   Which London team did Ipswich beat 6-1 away in the quarter-final of the FA Cup?

DIVISION ONE CHAMPIONS – 1961/1962

71.   How many of their 42 League matches did Ipswich win – 22, 24 or 26?

72.   Which team finished as runners-up in the League, three points behind The Tractor Boys?

73.   Which Town manager guided the club to this success?

74.   Who was Town's top League scorer with 33 goals?

75.   Following on from the previous question, who finished the season with 28 League goals?

76.   True or false: the club started the season with a draw and two defeats?

77.   Which team did Ipswich beat 2-0 on the last day of the season, during April 1962, to be crowned Champions, with Ray Crawford scoring a brace in the game?

78.   Against which club did Ray Crawford score a League hat-trick in Town's 5-2 home win during December 1961?

79.   What was the average attendance at Portman Road during this season – 22,863, 23,963 or 24,063?

80.   Can you name three of Town's goalscorers in their 6-2 home win against Sheffield United during August 1961, this being Town's first League win of the season?

JASON DOZZELL

81.   In which year was Jason born in Ipswich – 1966, 1967 or 1968?

82.   How old was Jason when he made his Ipswich Town debut, scoring in a 3-1 home win against Coventry City?

83.   Against which London team did Jason score a brace for Ipswich in their 2-2 home draw during October 1992 in the Premier League?

84.   True or false: Jason was capped at full international level for England whilst a Town player?

85.   How many League goals did Jason score for Ipswich in his football career – 50, 53 or 56?

86.   For which team did Jason sign when he left Portman Road in 1993?

87.   Which Town manager brought Jason back to Portman Road for his second playing spell at the club in 1997?

88.   For which Essex-based club did Jason play between 1998 and 2002?

89.   Which Blues manager handed Jason his Ipswich Town debut in February 1984?

90.   How many League games did Jason play for Ipswich during his playing career – 340, 360 or 380?

TERRY BUTCHER

91.   How many goals did Terry score for England in his 77 appearances for his country?

92.   Against which team did Terry make his Town debut during April 1978, in a 1-0 away defeat?

93.   How many League goals did Terry score for The Tractor Boys during the 1978/79 season?

94.   Which Town manager handed Terry his club debut in 1978?

95.   True or false: Terry managed Ipswich Town during the 1990s?

96.   In what position did Terry play during his playing days?

97.   What is Terry's middle name – Ian, Ivan or Ike?

98.   Against which team did Terry score for Town in their 1-0 away win in the UEFA Cup semi-final, 2nd leg, during April 1981?

99.   Terry scored Town's third goal in their 4-0 home League win against Everton during August 1980, but can you name one of the other scorers?

100.   For which Scottish club did Terry sign when he left Portman Road in 1986?

CLUB HONOURS

Match up the honour with the year it was achieved

101.	*Division One Champions*	*1961*
102.	*FA Cup Youth Winners*	*1982*
103.	*Texaco Cup Winners*	*1954*
104.	*Division One Runners-up*	*1957*
105.	*Division Two Champions*	*1973*
106.	*Division Three (South) Champions*	*1968*
107.	*Division Two Champions*	*1981*
108.	*Division Three (South) Champions*	*1992*
109.	*Division Two Champions*	*2005*
110.	*Division One Runners-up*	*1962*

UEFA CUP WINNERS – 1981

111. Which club did Ipswich beat 6-4 on aggregate in the 1st round during September and October 1980?

112. Following on from the previous question, who scored 4 goals for Town in the home leg when Ipswich won 5-1?

113. What was the aggregate score when Ipswich met Bohemians Praha in the 2nd round?

114. Which Town manager led the club to this success?

115. Who scored a hat-trick for Town when they beat Widzew Lodz 5-0 at home in the 3rd round, 1st leg, during November 1980?

116. By what scoreline did Ipswich beat St Etienne in the quarter-final match, 1st leg, away from home?

117. Which Town player scored the only goal in a 1-0 away win against FC Cologne in the semi-final, 2nd leg, during April 1981?

118. Can you name the three Town scorers in the UEFA Cup final, 1st leg, in a 3-0 home win during May 1981?

119. Which team did Ipswich beat in the final?

120. What was the aggregate score in the final?

NATIONALITIES – 1

Match up the player with his nationality

121.	Alan Lee	Bulgarian
122.	Jason de Vos	South African
123.	Matteo Sereni	Dutch
124.	Martijn Reuser	Irish
125.	Fabian Wilnis	Canadian
126.	Mich d'Avray	Jamaican
127.	Bontcho Guentchev	Dutch
128.	Mauricio Taricco	Dutch
129.	David Johnson	Italian
130.	Gus Uhlenbeek	Argentinian

IPSWICH TOWN V. COLCHESTER UNITED

131. Which two strikers scored for Town in their 2-1 home win over Colchester in the League Cup 2nd round during August 2008?

132. True or false: The clubs did not meet in any competitive competition during the 1980s and 1990s?

133. In which competition did the sides meet for the first time during the 1950/51 season?

134. What was the score when Ipswich beat The U's in the Championship at Portman Road during October 2007?

135. Which of the two teams finished highest in the Championship during the 2006/07 season?

136. Which Town defender was sent off in the 90th minute when the sides met at Portman Road in the Championship during January 2007?

137. Following on from the previous question, what was the score in the game at Portman Road?

138. True or false: the sides have never met in the FA Cup?

139. In which competition did the sides meet during the 1969/70 season?

140. Following on from the previous question, what was the score in the game at Portman Road?

LEGENDS – 1

Rearrange the letters to reveal the name of a club legend

141. **KIMC SLILM**

142. **LANAL RUTHEN**

143. **OSMIN TOMLIN**

144. **OHNJ KRAW**

145. **CIMK KELTSCOWL**

146. **LESLURS ONAMS**

147. **ECIR ETSGA**

148. **LUPA ECROPO**

149. **MOMYT EARPAK**

150. **LINCO JIVENOL**

TOWN MANAGERS

Match up the manager with the year he took charge at Portman Road

151.	Roy Keane	1955
152.	Jackie Milburn	1987
153.	George Burley	2002
154.	Bobby Robson	1963
155.	John Lyall	1994
156.	Alf Ramsey	2006
157.	Bobby Ferguson	2009
158.	Joe Royle	1969
159.	John Duncan	1990
160.	Jim Magilton	1982

UEFA CUP – 2002/2003

161. Which striker scored in the 90th minute in Town's 1-0 away win against Avenir Beggen in the qualifying 1st leg during August 2002?

162. What was the score when Avenir Beggen visited Portman Road to play the qualifying 2nd leg match during August 2002?

163. Which striker scored a hat-trick for Town against Avenir Beggen at Portman Road?

164. Which team did Town face in the 1st round of the UEFA Cup?

165. Following on from the previous question, what was the score in the 1st leg at Portman Road?

166. Which striker scored for Ipswich in their 1-0 away win in the 1st round, 2nd leg, during October 2002?

167. How many goals did Ipswich score in this competition during the 2002/03 season in the six UEFA Cup games?

168. Which Ipswich striker scored the only goal in a 1-0 home win in the 2nd round, 1st leg, during October 2002?

169. Who was manager of The Tractor Boys when the club was knocked out of the competition during November 2002?

170. Which team knocked Town out of the competition, finishing 1-1 on aggregate and then losing 4-2 on penalties away from home?

POSITIONS IN THE LEAGUE – 1

*Match up the season with the position
Town finished in the League*

171.	1980/81	22nd in Premier League
172.	1982/83	4th in Division One
173.	1984/85	16th in Premier League
174.	1986/87	17th in Division One
175.	1988/89	3rd in Division One
176.	1990/91	2nd in Division One
177.	1992/93	8th in Division Two
178.	1994/95	5th in Division Two
179.	1996/97	9th in Division One
180.	1998/99	14th in Division Two

WHERE DID THEY GO? – 1

*Match up the player with the team he joined
when he left Portman Road*

181.	Mick Stockwell	Peterborough United
182.	David Johnson	Sheffield Wednesday
183.	Bobby Petta	Everton
184.	Adam Tanner	Leicester City
185.	Jason Cundy	Celtic
186.	Alex Mathie	Colchester United
187.	Danny Sonner	Nottingham Forest
188.	Claus Thomsen	Dundee United
189.	Steve Sedgley	Portsmouth
190.	Stuart Slater	Wolves

TOWN IN THE LEAGUE CUP

191.   Which Town striker was the first player in the club's history to score 4 goals in a League Cup match, during September 1967 against Southampton?

192.   Against which team did Ipswich play their first League Cup game during October 1960, losing 2-0 at Portman Road?

193.   True or false: Town won this competition during the 1981/82 season?

194.   Which London team knocked Town out of the competition 4-1 on penalties after drawing 2-2 after extra time during January 1998 at Portman Road?

195.   Can you name the two Tractor Boys that scored against Arsenal in Town's 2-1 away win at Highbury during November 2000?

196.   Which team did Ipswich beat 4-0 at home in the 2nd round during September 1969?

197.   Which striker scored a brace for The Tractor Boys in a 2-1 away win against Burnley during October 1977?

198.   Which two Town midfielders scored the goals when Ipswich beat Brentford 2-0 at home in the 1st round during August 2004?

199.   Which Ipswich player scored two penalties against Northampton Town during the 2nd round in a 5-0 home win during August 1977?

200.   Which Tractor Boy scored a hat-trick in the competition against Wigan Athletic during October 1992?

BOBBY FERGUSON

201. In what position did Bobby play during his playing days?

202. How many of the 210 League games played while Bobby was in charge of The Tractor Boys did the club win – 71, 81 or 91?

203. Against which team did Town draw 1-1 away from home during August 1982, Bobby's first game in charge of The Tractor Boys?

204. True or false: in Bobby's first 6 League games in charge of Ipswich, the club drew 3 matches and lost 3 matches?

205. To what position in Division One did Bobby guide Ipswich during his first season in charge at Portman Road?

206. In which year was Bobby born – 1936, 1937 or 1938?

207. During 1982/83, while Bobby was in charge of Ipswich, what did the club fail to do for the first time in their history?

208. True or false: Bobby guided Town to 5th place in Division Two in his final season in charge at the club, 1986/87?

209. How many of their 48 Cup games did the club win while Bobby was in charge of The Tractor Boys – 22, 24 or 26?

210. True or false: Bobby played for Town during his playing days?

DIVISION ONE PLAY-OFF
FINAL WINNERS – 2000

211.   Which team did Ipswich beat in the play-off final?

212.   What was the score in the play-off final?

213.   Who played in goal for Town in the play-off final?

214.   At which stadium was the final played?

215.   Which defender scored Ipswich's first goal after 28
       minutes, levelling the score to 1-1?

216.   Which Dutch midfielder scored Town's last goal of the
       game in the 90th minute?

217.   Who was manager of the club when Ipswich won the
       play-off final?

218.   Can you name two of the three substitutes that Ipswich
       used in the play-off final?

219.   Which team did Ipswich beat 7-5 on aggregate in the
       play-off semi-finals?

220.   Which Town midfielder scored a hat-trick in the 5-3
       home win in the play-off semi-final, 2nd leg, during
       May 2000?

ALAN BRAZIL

221. How many League goals did Alan score for Ipswich in his career – 60, 70 or 80?

222. Against which team did Alan make his Ipswich debut, in a 2-1 away defeat during January 1978?

223. Against which club did Alan score a brace for The Tractor Boys in a 3-2 away win during December 1982 – Stoke City, Sunderland or Sheffield Wednesday?

224. How many Scotland caps did Alan win during his football career, scoring one goal for his country?

225. In which year was Alan born in Glasgow – 1957, 1958 or 1959?

226. Which London team did Alan join when he left Portman Road in 1983?

227. Against which team did Alan score all of Ipswich's 5 goals in a 5-2 home League win during February 1982?

228. How many League appearances did Alan make for Town in his football career – 134, 144 or 154?

229. In what position did Alan play during his playing days?

230. How many League goals did Alan score in 1981/82, finishing as Town's highest League scorer this season – 18, 20 or 22?

WHERE DID THEY COME FROM? – 1

*Match up the player with the club he played
for before joining Ipswich Town*

231.	Grant Leadbitter	Leicester City
232.	Alex Bruce	Bolton Wanderers
233.	Gareth McAuley	Cardiff City
234.	Richard Wright	Manchester United
235.	Tamás Priskin	Sheffield United
236.	Jonathan Walters	West Ham United
237.	Neil Alexander	Birmingham City
238.	Lee Martin	Watford
239.	Iván Campo	Sunderland
240.	Jon Stead	Chester City

UEFA CUP – 2001/2002

241. *Which Town defender scored in the 85th minute when Ipswich drew 1-1 with Torpedo Moscow at Portman Road in the 1st round, 1st leg, during September 2001?*

242. *Which Tractor Boy gave Town a 1-0 lead after 47 minutes against Torpedo Moscow in the 1st round, 2nd leg, in a 2-1 win away?*

243. *Following on from the previous question, who scored Ipswich's winner from the penalty spot after 54 minutes?*

244. *What was the score when Ipswich played Helsingborgs at Portman Road during October 2001 in the 2nd round, 1st leg?*

245. *Following on from the previous question, which Town striker scored a brace in the last ten minutes in the 3-1 away win against Helsingborgs in the 2nd round, 2nd leg?*

246. *True or false: Ipswich beat Inter Milan 1-0 in the 3rd round, 1st leg, at Portman Road during November 2001?*

247. *Following on from the previous question, who scored for Town?*

248. *Which Dutch team beat Inter Milan in the 2001/02 semi-finals and went on to win the competition in 2002/03, beating German team Borussia Dortmund in the final?*

249. *Which striker scored Town's only goal at the San Siro Stadium when Inter Milan beat Ipswich 4-1 in the 3rd round, 2nd leg, during December 2001?*

250. *Who managed Town during this UEFA Cup run?*

TOWN IN THE FA CUP

251.   Which London club did Town beat 3-0 at home in the FA Cup 4th round during January 1994, with Ian Marshall, Gavin Johnson and Neil Thompson scoring the goals?

252.   In which round did Town get knocked out of the competition by Liverpool during 1974?

253.   Who scored a hat-trick for The Tractor Boys against Halifax Town in the 3rd round of the competition during January 1976?

254.   Can you name the two Town scorers in the 2-1 away win against Blackpool in the 3rd round during January 2010?

255.   What was the score when Chesterfield visited Town at Portman Road in the 3rd round during January 2009?

256.   Can you name the three Town scorers in the 3-0 home win against Derby County in the 3rd round during January 2004?

257.   Which Town striker scored a hat-trick in the 3-0 away win in the 3rd round during January 1984?

258.   With which team did Town share a 4-4 draw at Portman Road in the 3rd round during January 1986?

259.   True or false: Town beat Manchester United 1-0 in the 4th round during January 1974, with Kevin Beattie scoring the goal?

260.   Which London team knocked Town out of the competition in the semi-finals during April 1975?

SQUAD NUMBERS – 2010/2011

Match up the player with the squad number he wore for Town during the 2010/2011 season

261.	Lee Martin	7
262.	Brian Murphy	14
263.	Alan Quinn	2
264.	David Norris	18
265.	Grant Leadbetter	8
266.	Jaime Peters	9
267.	Jonathan Stead	6
268.	Pablo Counago	1
269.	Carlos Edwards	15
270.	Connor Wickham	11

POSITIONS IN THE LEAGUE – 2

Match up the season with the position
Town finished in the League

271.	1981/82	7th in Division One
272.	1983/84	3rd in Division One
273.	1985/86	19th in Premier League
274.	1987/88	5th in Division One
275.	1989/90	20th in Division One
276.	1991/92	12th in Division One
277.	1993/94	9th in Division Two
278.	1995/96	2nd in Division One
279.	1997/98	8th in Division Two
280.	1999/2000	1st in Division Two

1960s

281. Who was Ipswich's captain during the 1961/62 season?

282. Against which team did Ipswich record their biggest win of the 1962/63 season, a 10-0 win at home in the European Cup?

283. True or false: at the start of the 1964/65 season Ipswich drew 3 and lost 5 League matches before winning their 9th League game, their longest start without a win since turning professional?

284. Who scored a Town hat-trick on his League debut in a 4-2 win against Portsmouth at Portman Road during the 1966/67 season?

285. True or false: between them, 6 different players scored 93 League goals for Ipswich during the 1961/62 season?

286. Against which team did Ipswich record their highest League attendance of 25,863 during the 1964/65 season?

287. Which player left Town to join Northampton during the 1965/66 season?

288. Who scored 12 League goals in only 15 appearances during the 1967/68 season?

289. From which club did Charlie Woods join Town during the 1966/67 season?

290. How many goals did Town concede in their 42 League games during 1963/64, a club record – 81, 101 or 121?

2009/2010

291. Ipswich had to wait until their 15th League game of the season for their first win, 1-0, with David Wright scoring the only goal against which club during October 2009?

292. With which team did Ipswich draw 1-1 at Portman Road on Boxing Day 2009?

293. Which striker scored a brace for Town against Queens Park Rangers at Portman Road in a 3-3 League draw during December 2009?

294. In what position in the League did the club finish?

295. Which on-loan striker scored his first goal for the club in a 1-1 away draw at Scunthorpe United during February 2010?

296. Who scored Ipswich's winner in the 85th minute in a 2-1 away win at Cardiff City during November 2009?

297. Who managed Town during this season?

298. Who finished as the club's highest League goalscorer with 8 goals?

299. Which striker scored a last-minute winner for the club in a 3-2 home win against Coventry City during January 2010?

300. Which midfielder scored his first goal for the club in a 1-0 away win against Sheffield Wednesday during February 2010?

KEVIN BEATTIE

301. How many League goals did Kevin score for Town in his career – 20, 22 or 24?

302. Which Town manager handed Kevin his club debut in 1972?

303. Against which Yorkshire club did Kevin score his first Town goal, in a 3-3 away draw during August 1972?

304. Kevin and which only other Tractor Boy started all 42 League games for Ipswich during the 1973/74 season?

305. Against which Yorkshire team did Kevin score a brace in a 3-2 home win in the FA Cup 3rd round during January 1974?

306. How many full international caps did Kevin win for England in his career, scoring one goal – 9, 19 or 29?

307. In what position did Kevin play during his playing days?

308. In which season did Kevin make his last League appearance for Town?

309. How many League games did Kevin play for Town in his career – 208, 218 or 228?

310. What is Kevin's middle name?

1970s

311.   Which Town defender was the club captain throughout the 1970s?

312.   True or false: Ipswich fielded the same starting 11 for 11 consecutive matches during the 1972/73 season?

313.   Which Tractor Boy was signed from Blackburn Rovers during 1971/72 and went on to be the club's most capped player?

314.   Who was the club's top League scorer with 13 goals during the 1975/76 season?

315.   Ipswich finished 3rd in Division One during 1976/77, with which two sides finishing above them?

316.   Which team did Town beat 7-0 in the League during February 1974, with Trevor Whymark and Bryan Hamilton both scoring braces in the game?

317.   Who was the only Tractor Boy to play in all 42 League games during 1976/77?

318.   Against which team did Ipswich record their highest attendance at Portman Road during March 1975 in the FA Cup 6th round?

319.   Which two players finished as the club's top League scorers with 7 goals apiece during the 1971/72 season?

320.   Which team did Town beat 7-0 in the League during November 1976, with Trevor Whymark scoring 4 of the goals?

2008/2009

321. In which position did Town finish in the Championship – 7th, 8th or 9th?

322. Which Welsh defender did Ipswich sign from Charlton Athletic during August 2008?

323. For which team did Tommy Miller sign when he left Portman Road during May 2009?

324. With how many goals did top League scorer Jon Stead finish the season?

325. Which Tractor Boy played in goal for Town in all 46 League games during this season?

326. Who scored for the club after 2 minutes in the first League game of the season, a 2-1 home defeat to Preston North End during August 2008?

327. Can you name Town's three goalscorers in their 3-2 home win over Norwich City during April 2009?

328. Which Irish midfielder scored a brace in the club's 3-1 away win against Plymouth Argyle during October 2008?

329. Which defender did Ipswich sign on a free transfer from Bolton Wanderers during August 2008?

330. How many of their 46 League matches did Ipswich win – 15, 16 or 17?

TED PHILLIPS

331. In which year was Ted born in Leiston – 1931, 1932 or 1933?

332. How many hat-tricks did Ted score for Town in Division Three South during the 1956/57 season?

333. Following on from the previous question, can you name three of the teams that Ted scored hat-tricks against?

334. How many League goals did Ted score for Town during his career – 151, 161 or 171?

335. True or false: Ted scored 41 League goals in 41 starts during the 1956/57 season?

336. What is Ted's middle name – John, James or Joseph?

337. For which team did Ted sign when he left Portman Road in the mid-1960s?

338. Can you name the Town manager who handed Ted his debut during the 1953/54 season?

339. Against which team did Ted score a hat-trick in the League in a 4-1 home win during August 1959?

340. How many League games did Ted play for Town in his football career – 239, 269 or 299?

BILL BAXTER

341.　In how many League games did Bill play for The Tractor Boys in his career – 400, 409 or 418?

342.　In what position did Bill play during his playing days?

343.　True or false: Bill made his Town debut against Norwich City in a 4-1 home win during December 1960?

344.　With which club did Bill end his professional playing career?

345.　How many League goals did Bill score for Town during the 1964/65 season?

346.　Which Ipswich manager handed Bill his Town debut during the 1960/61 season?

347.　Against which London team did Bill score his first Town League goal, in a 1-1 League away draw during October 1962?

348.　How many League goals did Bill score for Town in his career – 11, 21 or 31?

349.　In which year was Bill born in Edinburgh – 1938, 1939 or 1940?

350.　Which club signed Bill when he left Portman Road in March 1971?

ERIC GATES

351.   How many League goals did Eric score for Town in his career – 71, 73 or 75?

352.   Against which team did Eric score a Town hat-trick in a 4-0 home win during December 1979?

353.   True or false: Eric was Town's top League scorer during the 1983/84 and 1984/85 seasons?

354.   Which Town manager handed Eric his Ipswich debut during the 1973/74 season?

355.   Against which Spanish team did Eric score a brace in the European Cup Winners' Cup in a 2-1 home win in the quarter-final, 1st leg, during March 1979?

356.   In what position did Eric play during his playing days?

357.   Which club did Eric join when he left Portman Road?

358.   True or false: Eric won two full England caps during his football career?

359.   Against which team did Eric score a brace in Town's 4-0 away win on the last day of the 1978/79 League season?

360.   In which year was Eric born in Ferryhill – 1953, 1954 or 1955?

ALLAN HUNTER

361. For which country did Allan win 53 full international caps?

362. How many League appearances did Allan make for Ipswich Town in his career – 270, 280 or 290?

363. From which Lancashire-based team did Allan sign when he arrived at Portman Road?

364. In which season did Allan win the Player of the Year award at Ipswich?

365. How many League goals did Allan score in his 36 League starts for Town during the 1974/75 season?

366. Which Ipswich manager brought Allan to Portman Road?

367. Against which London team did Allan score Town's second goal in a 2-0 home win on Boxing Day 1975 in Division One?

368. For which Essex-based team did Allan sign when he left Portman Road?

369. How many League goals did Allan score for Ipswich in his career – 6, 7 or 8?

370. In what position did Allan play during his playing days?

FRANK YALLOP

371. True or false: Frank won the Player of the Year award at Ipswich during the 1987/88 season?

372. What is Frank's middle name – Walter, Wilson or William?

373. In what position did Frank play during his playing days?

374. How many full international caps did Frank win for Canada during his playing career – 52, 54 or 56?

375. True or false: Frank managed his country, Canada, between 2004 and 2006?

376. Against which team did Frank made his Ipswich League debut, in a 1-0 away defeat during March 1984?

377. How many League goals did Frank score for Town during his football career – 3, 5 or 7?

378. True or false: Frank scored twice for Ipswich during the 1988/89 season, both goals coming in 5-1 League wins?

379. Against which two teams did Frank score during 1992/93, Town's first season in the Premier League?

380. How many League games did Frank play for Ipswich in his career – 314, 316 or 318?

STEVE McCALL

381. How many League goals did Steve score for Town in his career – 6, 7 or 8?

382. In which year was Steve born in Carlisle – 1959, 1960 or 1961?

383. True or false: Steve played in all 42 League matches for Town during the 1983/84 season?

384. Which team did Steve join when he left Portman Road in 1987?

385. Against which country did Steve win his only England B cap during 1984?

386. What was the only winners' medal that Steve picked up during his Ipswich career?

387. What is Steve's middle name – Harold, Hilary or Howard?

388. True or false: Steve won the Ipswich Player of the Year award during the 1984/85 season?

389. Against which Midlands-based team did Steve score his only League goal of the 1983/84 season, in a 3-1 home win on Boxing Day 1983?

390. How many League appearances did Steve make for Town in his career - 257, 259 or 261?

MICK MILLS

391. How many League appearances did Mick make for Town in his career – 591, 601 or 611?

392. Which Town manager handed Mick his club debut during 1965/66?

393. What is Mick's middle name – David, Donald or Dennis?

394. Which manager made Mick Town's captain?

395. How many League goals did Mick score for Town in his career – 11, 22 or 33?

396. How old was Mick when he made his Town League debut, in a 5-2 win against Wolves?

397. In which year was Mick born in Godalming – 1947, 1949 or 1951?

398. True or false: Mick became the first player in Town's club history to make 100 League appearances before his 21st birthday?

399. Who were the opponents when Mick captained England for the first time in 1978?

400. How many full England caps did Mick win in his career?

PLAYER OF THE YEAR – 2

Match up the season with the player who won the award

401.	1999/2000	Mick Stockwell
402.	1998/99	John Wark
403.	1997/98	David Linighan
404.	1996/97	John Wark
405.	1995/96	James Scowcroft
406.	1994/95	Simon Milton
407.	1993/94	Craig Forrest
408.	1992/93	Matt Holland
409.	1991/92	Mauricio Taricco
410.	1990/91	Jamie Clapham

RICHARD WRIGHT

411. In which year was Richard born in Ipswich – 1976, 1977 or 1978?

412. How many England caps did Richard win during his playing career?

413. True or false: Richard was ever present for Town during the 1997/98, 1998/99 and 1999/2000 seasons?

414. What squad number did Richard wear for The Tractor Boys during the 2009/10 season – 1, 13 or 30?

415. What is Richard's middle name – Ian, Ivan or Ivor?

416. For which team did Richard sign when he left Portman Road in July 2001?

417. Against which team did Richard make his Town debut as a 17-year-old during May 1995 in a 2-0 home win?

418. True or false: Richard scored one League goal for The Tractor Boys during the 1999/2000 season?

419. For which team did Richard play between 2002 and 2007?

420. Which Town manager signed Richard during July 2008 for his second playing spell at the club?

SECOND DIVISION CHAMPIONS – 1991/1992

421.   Which team finished as runners-up, 4 points behind Town?

422.   Which Town manager led the club to this success?

423.   Which striker finished the season with 16 League goals?

424.   Which two players scored Ipswich's three goals in a 3-1 home win against Brighton & Hove Albion on the last day of the League season?

425.   Which London club did Ipswich beat 2-0 at home on Boxing Day 1991, with Chris Kiwomya scoring both goals?

426.   How many of their 46 League games did Town win – 24, 26 or 28?

427.   What was the average home attendance during this season – 14,247, 16,247 or 18,247?

428.   Can you name the two players that each scored a brace in a 5-2 home win against Portsmouth during February 1992?

429.   True or false: Ipswich won all 4 League games during August 1991?

430.   How many League goals did Jason Dozzell score during this season – 10, 11 or 12?

CAPPED TRACTOR BOYS – 1

*Match up the player with the number of caps
won for his country whilst a Blues player*

431.	Arnold Mühren	42 Canadian Caps
432.	Eric Gates	12 Danish Caps
433.	Claus Thomsen	21 Northern Irish Caps
434.	Matt Holland	42 English Caps
435.	Bryan Hamilton	26 Scottish Caps
436.	Frans Thijssen	7 Dutch Caps
437.	Craig Forrest	38 Canadian Caps
438.	John Wark	10 Dutch Caps
439.	Mick Mills	33 Irish Caps
440.	Frank Yallop	2 English Caps

PORTMAN ROAD

441. Which stand is situated on Portman Road, and is also the stand for visiting supporters?

442. How many turnstiles does the South Stand have?

443. What is the name of the road where the Sir Bobby Robson Stand is situated?

444. What stand is opposite the Cobbold Stand?

445. What is the stadium's postcode?

446. In what year did Ipswich Town move to Portman Road?

447. Can you name the two grounds in the town where the club played before moving to Portman Road?

448. Approximately how many yards is Portman Road from Ipswich railway station?

449. Which team did England play at Portman Road in 2003, a friendly that England won 3-1?

450. Outside the ground there are statues of which two legendary club managers?

IPSWICH TOWN V. NORWICH CITY

451.   True or false: Ipswich won the first two Premier League meetings, both played during the 1992/93 season?

452.   Who scored Town's winner in a 3-2 home League win against The Canaries during April 2009?

453.   What was the score when Ipswich visited Carrow Road in the League during February 2006?

454.   Which Town striker scored a hat-trick in a 5-0 home win in the League during February 1998?

455.   Which player scored Town's winner in a 2-1 home League win during December 1993?

456.   In what year did the teams first meet in the FA Cup?

457.   What was the score when the sides met in Division Two at Portman Road during December 1960?

458.   True or false: Ipswich beat Norwich City 2-0 at Portman Road and 2-0 at Carrow Road during the 1984/85 League season?

459.   Which club won the first League Cup meeting of the 1968/69 season?

460.   Which two players scored The Tractor Boys' two goals in a 2-0 win at Carrow Road during March 2003?

1980s

461.　Who was Town's captain during the 1985/86 season?

462.　Which striker was the club's top scorer during the 1987/88 season with 17 League goals in Division Two?

463.　Can you name the three managers in charge of the club during the 1980s?

464.　Which player did the club sign from Seaham Red Star during the 1985/86 season?

465.　True or false: Ipswich did not concede a League goal at the North End Stand end of Portman Road throughout the 1986/87 season?

466.　How old was John Jackson when he played a match for Ipswich during 1981/82, becoming the oldest player to represent the club?

467.　Which team did Ipswich beat 6-0 away from home during September 1982 in Division One?

468.　Can you name three of the four players that scored double figures during 1988/89?

469.　From which club did Ipswich sign Kevin Wilson during the 1984/85 season?

470.　Which player finished as the club's highest League scorer with only 7 goals during 1985/86?

2007/2008

471.   Which team did The Blues beat 4-1 at home on the opening day of the League season?

472.   Which player scored a hat-trick against Bristol City in a 6-0 home win during November 2007?

473.   Who was Ipswich manager during this season?

474.   In what position did Ipswich finish in the League at the end of this season?

475.   Which striker scored the club's only League goal in a 1-0 home win against Hull City on the final day of the League season?

476.   From which team did Ipswich sign Alan Quinn during January 2008?

477.   Can you name the three players that scored double figures in League competition during this season?

478.   Which Canadian defender played in all 46 League matches this season?

479.   Which midfielder scored his only Ipswich career League goal against Blackpool in a 2-1 home win during February 2008?

480.   Which striker scored a brace in a 4-1 home League win against Sheffield Wednesday during September 2007?

FRANS THIJSSEN

481. How many League goals did Frans score for Town in his career – 5, 10 or 15?

482. In what position did Frans play during his playing days?

483. Which Town manager signed Frans for the club in 1979?

484. Against which club did Frans score his first Ipswich goal, in a 1-0 away win during April 1979?

485. How many League appearances did Frans make for Town in his football career – 85, 125 or 165?

486. How much did Town pay FC Twente in February 1979 when Frans arrived at Portman Road?

487. In what year was Frans named Football Writers' Player of the Year?

488. Following on from the previous question, Frans was only the second foreign player to win this award, but who was the first, winning it in 1966 while playing for Manchester City?

489. For which English team did Frans play during 1983?

490. True or false: Frans scored in Town's UEFA Cup final, 2nd leg, in May 1981?

ARNOLD MÜHREN

491. How many League goals did Arnold score for Ipswich during the 1980/81 season?

492. Which English side did Arnold join when he left Ipswich in 1982?

493. With which winners' medal did Arnold leave Ipswich?

494. How many full international caps did Arnold win in his career for Holland, scoring three goals – 21, 23 or 25?

495. Against which team did Arnold score a brace for Town in a 5-1 home win during December 1978?

496. How many League goals did Arnold score for Ipswich during his career – 11, 21 or 31?

497. Against which team did Arnold make his Ipswich League debut, in a 3-0 home defeat during August 1978?

498. In which position did Arnold play during his playing days – defender, midfielder or striker?

499. From which Dutch side did Arnold sign when he joined Ipswich Town?

500. Which Town manager brought Arnold to Portman Road?

PAUL MARINER

501. How many times did Paul win the Player of the Year award at Portman Road?

502. True or false: Paul once scored four goals in a competitive match for Ipswich Town?

503. Against which team did Paul score his first Ipswich hat-trick during March 1977?

504. How many League goals did Paul score for Town in his career – 76, 96 or 116?

505. From which team did Paul join Ipswich?

506. How many League goals did Paul score in his 1976/77 season at Portman Road?

507. Which manager brought Paul to Portman Road?

508. How many League appearances did Paul make for Town in his career – 160, 260 or 360?

509. True or false: Paul was Town's top League scorer during the 1977/78, 1978/79 and 1979/80 seasons?

510. Against which team did Paul score a hat-trick in a 6-0 home win during March 1980?

MICK STOCKWELL

511. Against which team did Mick make his Town debut in a 1-0 away win on Boxing Day 1985?

512. True or false: Mick played in all 46 League games for Town during the 1991/92 season?

513. In which season did Mick win the Player of the Year award at Portman Road?

514. How many League goals did Mick score for Town in his career – 35, 37 or 39?

515. Against which team did Mick play in his Town testimonial in 1995?

516. Against which team did Mick score his first Town League goal, in a 2-1 away defeat during November 1986?

517. What is Mick's middle name – Thomas, Timothy or Trevor?

518. In which year did Mick leave Portman Road for Layer Road when he joined Colchester United?

519. How many League appearances did Mick make as a Town player – 406, 506 or 606?

520. In which year was Mick born in Chelmsford – 1963, 1964 or 1965?

RICHARD NAYLOR

521. Which Town manager handed Richard his Town debut in the 1990s?

522. Against which club did Richard score a brace for Town in a 3-0 home win on Boxing Day 1998?

523. In which year was Richard born in Leeds – 1977, 1978 or 1979?

524. Against which two sides was Richard sent off while playing for Ipswich during the 2005/06 season?

525. How many League goals did Richard score for Town in his career – 37, 38 or 39?

526. Which of the goals did Richard score in Town's 4-2 win over Barnsley in the 2000 play-off final at Wembley - 1st, 2nd, 3rd or 4th?

527. How many League goals did Richard score for Town during the 1996/97 season in his 19 starts and 8 substitute appearances?

528. What is Richard's middle name – Alan, Alvin or Aaron?

529. In what year did Richard leave Portman Road?

530. For which Yorkshire-based club did Richard sign when he left Ipswich Town?

DARREN BENT

531.   For which London club did Darren sign when he left Portman Road in June 2005?

532.   Against which team did Darren score the only goal for Town in a 1-0 home win during April 2002 in the Premier League?

533.   How many League goals did Darren score for Town in the 2002/03 season – 10, 11 or 12?

534.   Against which team did Darren score an Ipswich hat-trick in a 3-1 away win during March 2004?

535.   Against which team did Darren score the last goal of his Ipswich career, in a 2-2 home draw during April 2005?

536.   In which year was Darren born in Cambridge – 1983, 1984 or 1985?

537.   For which team did Darren sign during August 2009?

538.   How many League goals did Darren score for Town in his career – 43, 45 or 47?

539.   What is Darren's middle name – Ashley, Ainsley or Adam?

540.   How many League goals did Darren score for Town in the 2004/05 season – 15, 17 or 19?

MARTIJN REUSER

541.   How many full international Dutch caps did Martijn
       win for his country?

542.   From which Dutch team did Martijn join The Tractor
       Boys in 2000?

543.   Against which team did Martijn make his Blues debut,
       scoring a last-minute goal in a 1-0 home win during
       March 2000?

544.   How many League goals did Martijn score for The
       Blues in the Premier League during 2000/01?

545.   Against which team did Martijn score a brace for Town
       in a 3-1 home League win during March 2001?

546.   How many League goals did Martijn score for Ipswich
       in his football career – 12, 14 or 16?

547.   Martijn scored Town's first goal against Portsmouth in
       a 3-0 League home win during April 2003, but which
       two players scored the other goals?

548.   What is Martijn's middle name – Franciscus, Frederic or
       Franco?

549.   In which position did Martijn play during his playing
       days at Portman Road – defender, midfielder or
       striker?

550.   Against which team did Martijn score his last Town
       goal, in a 2-1 away League win during April 2004?

FABIAN WILNIS

551.   From which Dutch team did Fabian sign when he joined Ipswich Town during 1999?

552.   Against which team did Fabian score his first Town goal, in a 6-0 away win during April 1999?

553.   Which Town manager signed Fabian for The Tractor Boys?

554.   Fabian scored against Manchester United after six minutes in a Premier League match at Portman Road during August 2000, but who scored United's equaliser after 39 minutes, with the game ending 1-1?

555.   Fabian put Town 1-0 in front against Norwich City in the League during March 2003, but who scored the second goal to clinch a 2-0 win at Carrow Road?

556.   What is Fabian's middle name – Liam, Lee or Lloyd?

557.   Against which team did Fabian score a last-minute goal in a 1-0 away win during November 2000 in the Premier League?

558.   In which year was Fabian born – 1970, 1972 or 1974?

559.   Against which team did Fabian play his Ipswich testimonial match in 2009?

560.   For which Essex team did Fabian sign when he left Portman Road in 2008?

2006/2007

561. In which position did Ipswich finish in the League –
14th, 15th or 16th?

562. Which team finished higher in the League – Ipswich
Town or Norwich City?

563. Who was the club's top scorer with 16 League goals
this season?

564. Which team did The Blues beat 5-1 at Portman Road
during April 2007?

565. Which player scored an Ipswich brace in a 3-1 home
win against Cardiff City in May 2007?

566. Which team did The Blues beat 2-1 away on Boxing
Day 2006?

567. Which Town forward scored 7 League goals in his 4
starts and 27 substitute appearances this season?

568. True or false: The Blues failed to win one of their first
four League games?

569. Which goalkeeper started 11 League matches for Town
during this season?

570. Against which club did Alan Lee score a League
hat-trick in a 5-0 home win during October 2006?

CHRIS KIWOMYA

571.   Against which team did Chris make his Town League debut, in a 1-1 home draw during September 1988?

572.   True or false: Chris won one full England international cap during 1992?

573.   How many League appearances did Chris make for Ipswich in his football career – 225, 255 or 285?

574.   Against which team did Chris score his first Ipswich League goal, in a 4-2 away win during January 1989?

575.   Against which team did Chris score a Blues hat-trick in a 4-0 home win in the League Cup 2nd round, 2nd leg, during October 1992?

576.   How many League goals did Chris score for Town in his football career – 41, 51 or 61?

577.   What is Chris's middle name – Mark, Matthew or Martin?

578.   Which London club signed Chris when he left Portman Road in 1995?

579.   True or false: Chris was Town's top League scorer during the 1990/91, 1991/92 and 1992/93 seasons?

580.   Which manager gave Chris his Ipswich Town debut?

SIMON MILTON

581. Which Town manager signed Simon for the club in 1987?

582. In what position did Simon play during his playing days?

583. In which year was Simon born in Fulham – 1962, 1963 or 1964?

584. Against which team did Simon score Town's winning goal in a 3-2 away win on the final day of the 1987/88 season, during May 1988?

585. From which local team did Simon join Ipswich Town in 1987?

586. How many League goals did Simon score for Ipswich in his career – 38, 48 or 58?

587. What is Simon's middle name – Charles, Christopher or Colin?

588. Against which club did Simon score his only Ipswich Town hat-trick, in a 5-1 away win during September 1988?

589. True or false: Simon was the club's Player of the Year for the 1995/96 season?

590. How many League appearances did Simon make for Ipswich Town in his football career – 279, 280 or 281?

ROMEO ZONDERVAN

591.   True or false: Romeo was the club's Player of the Year for the 1986/87 season?

592.   How many League goals did Romeo score for Ipswich in his career – 11, 12 or 13?

593.   From which Midlands-based club did Romeo join The Tractor Boys in 1984?

594.   True or false: Romeo was capped at full international level in 1981, playing for Holland?

595.   In which year was Romeo born – 1958, 1959 or 1960?

596.   Which Town manager brought Romeo to Portman Road?

597.   Against which team did Romeo make his Ipswich debut, in a 0-0 home draw during March 1984?

598.   True or false: Romeo is a fully qualified pilot?

599.   For which Dutch team did Romeo sign when he left Portman Road in 1992?

600.   How many League appearances did Romeo make for Town in his career - 272, 274 or 276?

JIM MAGILTON

601. From which club did Jim sign, initially on loan during January 1999 and then permanently for Ipswich Town during March 1999?

602. At which top-flight club was Jim an apprentice?

603. True or false: the first managerial appointment of Jim's career was at Ipswich in 2006?

604. Jim took over from which manager at Portman Road?

605. How many League goals did Jim score in his Ipswich Town career –16, 17 or 18?

606. In which year was Jim born in Belfast – 1968, 1969 or 1970?

607. True of false: Jim's only career hat-trick was while playing for Town against Bolton Wanderers in a play-off semi-final, 2nd leg, 5-3 home win during May 2000?

608. Jim scored one League goal in Town's 2000/01 Premier League season, in a 2-1 away defeat against which team during September 2000?

609. Against which club did Jim score Town's first goal in the 4-1 League win at Portman Road during May 1999, on the final day of the League season?

610. In what position did Jim play during his playing days at Portman Road?

JOHN WARK

611. How many League goals did John score for Ipswich in his career – 133, 134 or 135?

612. John was given a small part in which 1981 film, playing alongside Pelé and Bobby Moore?

613. Which two awards did John receive in 1981?

614. True or false: John finished the 1980/81 season with 36 competitive goals for Town?

615. How many full Scottish caps did John win for his country, scoring seven goals – 20, 29 or 38?

616. For which club did John play between 1984 and 1988?

617. What is the name of John's autobiography, published in 2009?

618. With how many League goals did John end the 1982/83 season, finishing as the club's highest scorer?

619. How many playing spells did John have at the club – 2, 3 or 4?

620. John scored four Town goals in a 6-1 win against which club, in a Division One match during October 1982?

KIERON DYER

621. For which team did Kieron sign when he left Portman Road in July 1999?

622. In which year was Kieron born in Ipswich – 1977, 1978 or 1979?

623. How many League goals did Kieron score for Ipswich in his football career – 11, 21 or 31?

624. For how many seasons was Kieron an Ipswich Town player?

625. For which London club did Kieron sign in 2007?

626. Against which team did Kieron score Ipswich's third goal in a 4-1 home League win during May 1999, with Jim Magilton, James Scowcroft and Richard Naylor scoring the other goals?

627. What is Kieron's middle name – Clive, Chester or Courtney?

628. Which Town manager handed Kieron his club debut?

629. True or false: Kieron never played a game for Ipswich Town in the Premier League?

630. Against which team did Kieron score Town's 90th-minute winner in a 2-1 away League win during February 1998, with Alex Mathie scoring the first goal in the 83rd minute?

1990s

631.   Against which club did Ipswich achieve their record League attendance of 22,093, in May 1993, during their first season in the Premier League?

632.   Who was Town's top scorer with just five League goals during the 1994/95 season?

633.   Which striker scored in the club's first three League matches of the 1993/94 season?

634.   Against which team did Adam Tanner score Town's only goal in a 1-0 away win during January 1995, the club's first ever win at the opponents' stadium?

635.   Who was club captain during the 1996/97, 1997/98 and 1998/99 seasons?

636.   Against which team did Ipswich record their biggest victory of the 1994/95 season, a 4-1 home win during January 1995, with Chris Kiwomya scoring a brace?

637.   How much was a match-day programme during the 1993/94 season?

638.   Who became the club's first ever goalkeeping substitute when Craig Forrest was sent off in a home match against Sheffield United during September 1992?

639.   From which club did Ipswich sign Jason Cundy during the 1996/97 season?

640.   Who scored Town's winner, their 3,000th goal in the Football League, in a 2-1 home win against Middlesbrough during August 1991?

POT LUCK - 1

641. True or false: in 2006 the club donated 500 orange and blue-and-white shirts to children in Iraq?

642. Can you name the three colours that make up the Ipswich Town crest?

643. Who was the club's shirt sponsor during the 1992/93 season?

644. How much was a match-day programme during the 2009/10 season?

645. True or false: when Roy Keane was appointed as Ipswich manager in 2009 he became the first Irish manager in the club's history?

646. Who was the club's chief executive during the 2009/10 season?

647. Can you name three of the five former Town managers whose first names start with the letter 'J'?

648. In what year did Ipswich Town last play in the top flight, in the Premier League?

649. How many times have Town participated in European competition?

650. Who was the club's shirt sponsor during the 1998/99 season?

2005/2006

651.   In which position did Ipswich finish in the League –
       13th, 15th or 17th?

652.   Which Welsh midfielder signed for Town from West
       Ham United during January 2006?

653.   Which Spanish midfielder signed for Town in July 2005
       and picked up two red cards, one against Sheffield
       United and the other against Norwich City, both
       during September 2005?

654.   Can you name the French midfielder that started 24
       matches and made 10 substitute appearances for Town
       during this season?

655.   With how many League goals did striker Sam Parkin
       finish the season?

656.   Can you name the two goalkeepers that played for
       Town this season?

657.   Which team did Ipswich beat 1-0 at home on the
       opening day of the League season?

658.   Which striker signed for Town from Cardiff City during
       January 2006?

659.   Who managed Ipswich during this season, his last
       season in charge at Portman Road prior to Jim
       Magilton taking over in the summer?

660.   Who finished as the club's highest scorer with only
       seven League goals?

RUSSELL OSMAN

661. What is Russell's middle name – Christopher, Charles or Clive?

662. In what position did Russell play during his playing days?

663. True or false: Russell won 11 full international caps for England during his career?

664. Against which London team did Russell score Town's second goal in a 2-0 away win during April 1980, with Paul Mariner scoring the first goal?

665. In which year was Russell born in Repton, Derbyshire - 1959, 1960 or 1961?

666. For which club did Russell sign when he left Portman Road in 1985?

667. How many League goals did Russell score for Town in his career – 15, 17 or 19?

668. Against which London team did Russell make his Ipswich League debut, in a 1-0 home win during September 1977?

669. Which club did Russell manage between 1996 and 1998?

670. In how many matches did Russell play for Town in his career – 292, 293 or 294?

PAUL COOPER

671. How many League appearances did Paul make for Ipswich Town in his career – 447, 457 or 467?

672. In what position did Paul play during his playing days?

673. What is Paul's middle name – David, Daniel or Donald?

674. From which club did Paul join Ipswich Town in 1974?

675. How many of the 49 penalties that Paul faced did he save as an Ipswich player – 17, 18 or 19?

676. For which team did Paul play during the 1990/91 season?

677. Which two winners' medals did Paul win while an Ipswich player?

678. In which year was Paul born in Brierley Hill, Staffordshire – 1951, 1953 or 1955?

679. True or false: Paul won a full international cap for England during the 1970s?

680. Which team did Paul join when he left Portman Road in 1987?

CLIVE WOODS

681. In what position did Clive play during his playing days?

682. Against which team did Clive make his Ipswich League debut, in a 2-0 home win during September 1969?

683. How many League appearances did Clive make for Town - 267, 277 or 287?

684. Against which team did Clive score the club's only goal in a 1-0 home League win during September 1974?

685. In which year was Clive born in Norwich – 1947, 1948 or 1949?

686. True or false: Clive was voted Man of the Match the 1978 FA Cup final against Arsenal?

687. Against which team did Clive score a brace in a 2-0 away win during October 1976 in Division One?

688. How many League goals did Clive score during his Ipswich career – 22, 24 or 26?

689. What is Clive's middle name – Richard, Roger or Raymond?

690. For which team did Clive sign when he left Portman Road in 1980?

BRYAN HAMILTON

691.   How many League games did Bryan play for Town in his career - 153, 155 or 157?

692.   Against which team did Bryan score his first Ipswich Town goal, in a 3-1 home League win during August 1971?

693.   Which manager brought Bryan to Portman Road?

694.   With which other Ipswich player did Bryan finish as Town's highest League goalscorer with 11 goals during the 1972/73 season?

695.   Against which team did Bryan score a brace for Town in their 4-1 home win during February 1973?

696.   True or false: Bryan finished as Town's highest League goalscorer with 16 goals from 42 appearances during the 1973/74 season?

697.   Bryan won 50 international caps and scored four goals for which country, going on to manage them between 1994 and 1998?

698.   Against which team did Bryan score a Town hat-trick in a 5-4 home win during March 1975?

699.   For which team did Bryan sign when he left Portman Road in 1976?

700.   How many League goals did Bryan score for The Tractor Boys in his career – 23, 43 or 63?

JOHN LYALL

701. In what year did John take charge of Ipswich Town?

702. Which Town goalkeeper did John sign from Coventry City during the 1992/93 season?

703. Which London club did John manage in the 1970s and 1980s?

704. In which year was John born in Ilford – 1939, 1940 or 1941?

705. How many games did Ipswich win during John's 38 Cup games in charge at the club – 10, 13 or 16?

706. True or false: John managed the England national team during the 1990s?

707. In which position did John play during his playing days – defender, midfielder or striker?

708. True or false: John guided Town to the Second Division Championship in only his second League season in charge at Portman Road?

709. How many of the 193 League games played under John's management did Ipswich win – 61, 81 or 101?

710. What was John's middle name – Angus, Arthur or Anthony?

WHERE DID THEY COME FROM? – 2

Match up the player with the club he played for before joining Ipswich Town

711.	Darren Currie	Sheffield Wednesday
712.	Jason de Vos	Tranmere Rovers
713.	Georges Santos	Norwich City
714.	Neill Rimmer	Brighton & Hove Albion
715.	Steve Whitton	Everton
716.	Jamie Clapham	Blackburn Rovers
717.	John McGreal	Wigan Athletic
718.	Eddie Youds	Grimsby Town
719.	Andy Marshall	Tottenham Hotspur
720.	Marcus Bent	Everton

LEGENDS – 2

Rearrange the letters to reveal the name of a club legend

721. LIBL TAXREB

722. GUDO SERE

723. SANJO ZELDLOZ

724. KARNF LOPAYL

725. YOR LABIYE

726. MYJMI BATTLEDERE

727. OHNJ WHOLETRYS

728. EGGROE RULEBY

729. TAMT NODHALL

730. IJM ANTIGLOM

POSITIONS IN THE LEAGUE – 3

*Match up the season with the position Town
finished in the League*

731. 1961/62   18th in Division One

732. 1963/64   3rd in Division One

733. 1965/66   18th in Division One

734. 1967/68   6th in Division One

735. 1969/70   1st in Division Two

736. 1971/72   1st in Division One

737. 1973/74   22nd in Division One

738. 1975/76   13th in Division One

739. 1977/78   15th in Division Two

740. 1979/80   4th in Division One

2004/2005

741. Which team did Town beat 2-1 on the opening day of the League season, with Richard Naylor and Dean Bowditch scoring the goals?

742. Which Yorkshire-based side did Ipswich beat 5-1 at Portman Road during November 2004?

743. Which midfielder scored a brace in Town's 6-0 home win against Nottingham Forest during March 2005?

744. Which London team beat Ipswich 4-2 on aggregate in the play-off semi-finals?

745. Who was Town's manager during this season?

746. Which midfielder signed for Ipswich from West Ham United during July 2004?

747. Can you name the Town midfielder that scored seven League goals this season?

748. Which two Town strikers finished the season with 19 League goals apiece?

749. In which position did Town finish in the League – 3rd, 4th or 5th?

750. Which midfielder signed for The Tractor Boys from Brighton & Hove Albion during December 2004?

1992/1993 – FIRST PREMIER LEAGUE SEASON

751.   In what position did Town finish in the League?

752.   Which team did Town play in their first ever Premier League match, a 1-1 home draw during August 1992?

753.   Following on from the previous question, who scored the club's first Premier League goal?

754.   Who managed The Tractor Boys during this season?

755.   True or false: Ipswich were unbeaten in their first eight Premier League matches?

756.   Which central defender was the only Town player to play in all 42 League matches during this season?

757.   Which striker was signed from Sporting Lisbon during this season?

758.   How many League games did Town win this season – 8, 10 or 12?

759.   Which Tractor Boy scored a brace against Norwich City in a 3-1 home win during April 1993?

760.   With how many League goals did top scorer Chris Kiwomya finish the season – 8, 9 or 10?

ROGER OSBORNE

761. How many League goals did Roger score during his Town career – 8, 9 or 10?

762. True or false: Roger won the Player of the Year award once during his Town football career?

763. In what position did Roger play during his time at Portman Road?

764. Against which Midlands team did Roger score Town's only goal in a 1-0 away League win during December 1974?

765. For which Essex-based team did Roger sign when he left Portman Road during February 1981?

766. Why did Roger miss the entire 1978/79 season at Portman Road?

767. How many League games did Roger play for Town during his career – 124, 134 or 144?

768. In which year was Roger born in Otley – 1950, 1955 or 1960?

769. Against which team did Roger make his Town League debut, in a 2-0 home win during October 1973?

770. Which Town manager handed Roger his debut at Portman Road?

TREVOR WHYMARK

771. Against which team did Trevor score four Town goals in a 7-0 home win in Division One during November 1976?

772. Trevor finished as the club's top scorer during the 1976/77 season, with how many League goals?

773. What is Trevor's middle name – John, James or Joseph?

774. How many League goals did Trevor score for Town in his career – 35, 55 or 75?

775. Against which team did Trevor score a hat-trick in a 5-0 home win during February 1977?

776. Against which Italian team did Trevor score four goals in a UEFA Cup 4-0 away win during October 1973?

777. Which manager handed Trevor his Town League debut?

778. In what position did Trevor play during his playing days?

779. In how many League games did Trevor play for Ipswich Town – 241, 261 or 281?

780. How many League goals did Trevor score for Town in his 36 League starts during the 1976/77 season?

COLIN VILJOEN

781. Against which team did Colin score a Division Two League hat-trick in a 4-3 away win for Town during February 1968?

782. True or false: Colin won Town's Player of the Year award during the 1974/75 season?

783. How many League appearances did Colin make for The Tractor Boys during his Town career – 205, 305 or 405?

784. Colin was Town's top League scorer during the 1969/70 season, with how many goals?

785. Against which team did Colin score a Division Two hat-trick in a 4-2 home win during March 1967?

786. Against which team did Colin score a brace for Ipswich in a 4-0 home win during September 1970?

787. In what position did Colin play during his playing days?

788. Which team did Colin join when he left Portman Road in 1978?

789. In which country was Colin born in 1948?

790. How many League goals did Colin score in his Ipswich Town career – 25, 45 or 65?

ROY STEPHENSON

791. Which manager signed Roy for Ipswich Town?

792. How many League goals did Roy score for Town in his playing career – 11, 21 or 31?

793. Against which club did Roy score his first Ipswich League goal, in a 3-3 home draw during September 1960?

794. From which club did Roy sign when he joined Ipswich Town?

795. In what year did Roy leave Portman Road to join Lowestoft Town?

796. Against which team did Roy make his Town debut, in a 4-0 home win during September 1960?

797. How many League appearances did Roy make for Town in his career – 144, 155 or 166?

798. How many League goals did Roy score in his 33 League appearances during his first season at Portman Road, 1960/61?

799. True or false: Roy scored Town's only goal in the Charity Shield 5-1 defeat against Tottenham during August 1962?

800. In which year was Roy born in Crook – 1930, 1931 or 1932?

PLAYER OF THE YEAR – 3

Match up the season with the player who won the award

801.	1989/90	Romeo Zondervan
802.	1988/89	Paul Mariner
803.	1987/88	Paul Cooper
804.	1986/87	Terry Butcher
805.	1985/86	Trevor Putney
806.	1984/85	John Wark
807.	1983/84	Alan Brazil
808.	1982/83	Frank Yallop
809.	1981/82	John Wark
810.	1980/81	Terry Butcher

PABLO COUÑAGO

811.   What squad number did Pablo wear for Town during the 2009/10 season?

812.   For which club did Pablo play in between his two playing spells at Portman Road?

813.   What nationality is Pablo?

814.   How many League goals did Pablo score for Town during the 2002/03 season – 15, 16 or 17?

815.   Against which team did Pablo score both goals for Town in their 2-1 home win during October 2003?

816.   In which year was Pablo born – 1978, 1979 or 1980?

817.   From which Spanish side did Pablo sign when he joined Ipswich Town in 2001?

818.   True or false: Pablo won caps for his country at Under 17, Under 18, Under 20 and Under 21 level?

819.   In what position does Pablo play?

820.   Against which club did Pablo score a brace in a 2-2 home League draw during October 2008?

MATT HOLLAND

821. How many goals did Matt score in his 49 appearances for the Republic of Ireland?

822. From which team did Matt join Town in 1997?

823. In which year was Matt born in Bury – 1973, 1974 or 1975?

824. How many League goals has Matt scored for Ipswich in his career – 30, 38 or 46?

825. Which Ipswich manager signed Matt for The Tractor Boys?

826. In what position did Matt play for Ipswich Town?

827. Against which team did Matt score a brace, including the winning goal in the 116th minute, in a 3-2 home win in the play-off semi final, 2nd leg, during May 1999?

828. Against which team did Matt score his first Town goal, in a 3-2 home defeat during September 1997?

829. What is Matt's middle name – Rhys, Ryan or Richard?

830. How many League goals did Matt score for Town in his first season at the club, 1997/98?

JOE ROYLE

831. How many of the 170 League matches played while Joe was in charge of the club did Ipswich win – 74, 76 or 78?

832. In what year did Joe take over at Portman Road?

833. In what position did Joe play during his playing days?

834. To what position in the League did Joe guide Town during his first full season in charge at Portman Road?

835. Which team did The Blues beat 4-2 at home in the League, recording Joe's first win as Town manager?

836. In which year was Joe born in Liverpool – 1946, 1949 or 1952?

837. Who was Town's caretaker manager before Joe took charge of Ipswich?

838. Can you name the two clubs that Joe played for and later went on to manage?

839. How many times did Joe lead Town to the play-offs, trying to get the club promoted to the Premier League?

840. Which season was Joe's last as Ipswich Town manager?

NATIONALITIES – 2

Match up the player with his nationality

841.	Frans Thijssen	Finnish
842.	Alan Brazil	Northern Irish
843.	Gerard Baker	Bermudian
844.	Gareth McAuley	Canadian
845.	Giovani dos Santos	Dutch
846.	Reggie Lambe	American
847.	Finidi George	Welsh
848.	Shefki Kuqi	Scottish
849.	Gavin Williams	Mexican
850.	Jaime Peters	Nigerian

CAPPED TRACTOR BOYS – 2

*Match up the player with the number of caps won
for his country whilst a Blues player*

851.	Kevin Beattie	6 Canadian Caps
852.	Richard Wright	7 Bulgarian Caps
853.	Alan Brazil	7 Finnish Caps
854.	Gavin Williams	4 Jamaican Caps
855.	Jason de Vos	1 English Cap
856.	Bontcho Guentchev	7 Nigerian Caps
857.	Hermann Hreidarsson	11 Scottish Caps
858.	Shefki Kuqi	9 English Caps
859.	David Johnson	16 Icelandic Caps
860.	Finidi George	1 Welsh Cap

WHERE DID THEY GO? – 2

*Match up the player with the team he joined
when he left Portman Road*

861.	Dean Bowditch	Rangers
862.	Richard Naylor	Bristol City
863.	Alan Lee	Sunderland
864.	Darren Ambrose	Doncaster Rovers
865.	Kelvin Davis	Derby County
866.	Alun Armstrong	Leeds United
867.	Kevin Horlock	Crystal Palace
868.	Gavin Williams	Yeovil Town
869.	Neil Alexander	Darlington
870.	Lewis Price	Newcastle United

POT LUCK – 2

871. Which manager has the all-time record for the largest percentage of Ipswich Town victories in the League?

872. Which Town player wore the squad number 35 during the 2009/10 season?

873. With which country did Ben Thatcher win seven full international caps?

874. Which Argentinian defender signed for Ipswich during January 2009?

875. Which goalkeeper did Roy Keane sign in January 2010?

876. True or false: Ipswich once had a Welsh manager, in charge in the 1950s?

877. In what year did Ipswich win the Amsterdam 700 Tournament?

878. What cup did Ipswich win in 1963?

879. What was the main colour of Ipswich's away strip during the 2009/10 season?

880. Against which team did Lee Martin score his first Town League goal, in a 3-3 away draw during September 2009, with Jack Colback and Tamas Priskin scoring the other Town goals?

2000/2001

881.   In which position in the Premier League did the club finish – 3rd, 4th or 5th?

882.   Can you name the two goalkeepers that played in the League during this season?

883.   Who was the only Tractor Boy to play in all 38 League games this season?

884.   Marcus Stewart finished as the club's highest League scorer, with how many goals?

885.   Which defender did Ipswich sign from Wimbledon during August 2000?

886.   Which striker scored Ipswich's goal against Liverpool after 45 minutes in a 1-0 away win at Anfield?

887.   What was the score when Tottenham Hotspur visited Portman Road during December 2000?

888.   Which defender scored Town's only goal in a 1-0 home League win over Sunderland during August 2000, to record the club's first League win of the season?

889.   Which manager was in charge at Portman Road during this season?

890.   How many of their 38 League games did Ipswich win – 16, 18 or 20?

JOHN ELSWORTHY

891. True or false: John was capped by his country, Wales, in his career?

892. Against which team did John make his Town debut, in a 4-0 defeat during December 1949?

893. How many League appearances did John make for Ipswich Town in his football career – 378, 388 or 398?

894. True or false: John won a Third Division South, Second Division and First Division winners' medal during his career?

895. Against which team did John score a Town hat-trick in a 4-1 home win in Division Three South during December 1953?

896. Which manager handed John his Town debut?

897. From which team did John join Town?

898. Against which team did John score the only European Ipswich goal of his career?

899. How many League goals did John score for Town in his career – 33, 44 or 55?

900. In what position did John play during his playing days?

JIMMY LEADBETTER

901. In which year was Jimmy born in Edinburgh – 1918, 1928 or 1938?

902. From which team did Ipswich sign Jimmy?

903. How many League appearances did Jimmy make for Town in his career – 344, 346 or 348?

904. Against which team did Jimmy score a Town hat-trick in the FA Cup 3rd round during January 1963, in a 3-2 away win?

905. How many League goals did Jimmy score for The Blues during the 1956/57 season?

906. Against which team did Jimmy make his Town debut, in a 1-0 home win during October 1955?

907. True or false: Jimmy played as a central defender during his playing days?

908. Which manager handed Jimmy his Blues debut in 1955?

909. How many League goals did Jimmy score for Town in his career – 13, 43 or 73?

910. For which non-League team did Jimmy sign when he left Portman Road?

BRIAN TALBOT

911.   *Against which team did Brian make his Town debut, in a 1-0 home win during February 1974?*

912.   *In what position did Brian play during his playing days?*

913.   *Which Town manager handed Brian his Ipswich debut in 1974?*

914.   *In how many League games did Brian play for Ipswich Town in his career – 177, 187 or 197?*

915.   *Against which team did Brian score a brace in a 4-1 away win during September 1974?*

916.   *Which London team did Brian join when he left Portman Road?*

917.   *What is Brian's middle name – Ernest, Edward or Edgar?*

918.   *Against which country did Brian make his England debut in 1977?*

919.   *How many League goals did Brian score for Ipswich in his career – 21, 23 or 25?*

920.   *In which year was Brian born in Ipswich – 1952, 1953 or 1954?*

DAVID LINIGHAN

921. Against which London team did David score in a 1-1 home draw during December 1993?

922. In how many of Town's 42 Premier League matches during the 1993/94 season did David play?

923. True or false: David was Ipswich captain for five seasons during the 1990s?

924. How many League goals did David score for The Tractor Boys in his career – 12, 14 or 16?

925. Which team did David join when he left Portman Road?

926. From which team did David join Town during the 1988/89 season?

927. How many League appearances did David make for The Tractor Boys in his career – 277, 287 or 297?

928. Against which team did David score his first Town League goal, in a 2-0 home win during January 1989?

929. Which manager brought David to Portman Road?

930. True or false: David was the only player to play in all 42 matches in the club's first Premier League season, 1992/93?

JAMES SCOWCROFT

931. In which year was James born in Bury St Edmunds – 1973, 1974 or 1975?

932. Which manager handed James his debut during the 1995/96 season?

933. How many League goals did James score during his first season as a Town player, 1995/96?

934. Against which team did James make his Town debut, in a 2-1 home defeat during October 1995?

935. Against which team did James score his only Ipswich League hat-trick, in a 3-0 away win during November 1998?

936. James was joint-top League scorer with 13 goals during the 1998/99 season, with which other player?

937. During which season was James Town's Player of the Year?

938. Which team did James join when he left Portman Road in 2001?

939. How many League goals did James score for Town in his career – 37, 47 or 57?

940. In which year did James return to Portman Road for a second spell, on loan at The Blues?

TOMMY MILLER

941. How many playing spells has Tommy had at Portman Road in his career – 2, 3 or 4?

942. What is Tommy's middle name – Wayne, William or Warren?

943. Against which club did Tommy score a brace for Town in a 5-1 home win during April 2005?

944. After good form in the 2004/05 season Tommy was called up for which country by Berti Vogts, but missed out due to an ankle injury?

945. From which club did George Burley sign Tommy in 2001?

946. Against which team did Tommy score a brace in Town's 6-0 home League win during March 2005?

947. Against which London club did Tommy score a brace for Town in a 4-1 home win on New Year's Day 2003?

948. In which year was Tommy born – 1978, 1979 or 1980?

949. For which club did Tommy sign when he left Portman Road during May 2009?

950. How many League goals did Tommy score for Ipswich during the 2002/03 season?

ALAN LEE

951.   From which team did Alan sign when he arrived at Portman Road during January 2006?

952.   Against which team did Alan make his Ipswich debut, in a 1-1 home draw during January 2006?

953.   How many League goals did Alan score for Town during the 2006/07 season – 15, 16 or 17?

954.   Against which team did Alan score an Ipswich hat-trick in a 5-0 home win during October 2006?

955.   For which country has Alan won full international caps?

956.   For which team did Alan sign when he left Portman Road during August 2008?

957.   Against which team did Alan score a brace in a 4-1 home win on the opening day of the 2007/08 League season?

958.   What is Alan's middle name – Meggs, Malachy or Magnus?

959.   Against which team did Alan score his first goals for Ipswich, both of them in a 2-0 away win during January 2006?

960.   Which manager signed Alan for Ipswich Town?

GERAINT WILLIAMS

961.   What was Geraint's nickname whilst at Town?

962.   How many Welsh caps did Geraint win for his country?

963.   In which year did Geraint join Town?

964.   Against which team did Geraint score Town's second
        goal in a 2-0 home win during November 1994?

965.   How many League goals did Geraint score whilst a
        Town player?

966.   Which manager brought Geraint to Portman Road?

967.   Against which team did Geraint make his Town League
        debut, in a 1-1 home draw during August 1992, Town's
        first Premier League game?

968.   How many League appearances did Geraint make for
        Town during his football career – 187, 217 or 247?

969.   For which team did Geraint sign when he left Portman
        Road in 1998?

970.   In how many of Town's 42 Premier League games did
        Geraint play during their first Premier League season,
        1992/93?

2001/2002

971.   With which team did Ipswich share a 3-3 away draw during October 2001, with Marcus Stewart scoring a brace in the game?

972.   What was the score when Sunderland visited Portman Road during December 2001 in the Premier League, with Alun Armstrong scoring a brace in the game?

973.   From which Lancashire-based team did Marcus Bent sign to join Town during November 2001?

974.   Which London team did Ipswich beat 2-1 away during December 2001, with Alun Armstrong scoring the winning goal in the 88th minute?

975.   Who was Town's manager this season?

976.   In which position in the Premier League did Ipswich finish – 17th, 18th or 19th?

977.   With how many League goals did Town's top scorer Marcus Bent finish the season?

978.   Can you name the two Town players, a defender and a midfielder, that played in all 38 League matches during this season?

979.   Which striker did Ipswich sign from Real Mallorca during August 2001?

980.   Which Town striker scored a brace in a 2-2 away draw against Newcastle United during March 2002?

JONATHAN WALTERS

981. What squad number did Jonathan wear for Town during the 2009/10 season?

982. From which club did Jonathan sign when he joined Ipswich?

983. Which manager signed Jonathan for The Tractor Boys?

984. Against which Welsh team did Jonathan score a brace in Town's 3-1 home win during May 2007?

985. How many League goals did Jonathan score for Ipswich during the 2007/08 season?

986. Against which team did Jonathan score a Town hat-trick in a 6-0 home win during November 2007?

987. In which year was Jonathan born in Birkenhead – 1981, 1982 or 1983?

988. Against which team did Jonathan make his Town debut, in a 0-0 away draw during January 2007?

989. Against which London club did Jonathan score his first Town goal, the winning goal in a 2-1 home win during March 2007?

990. Against which team did Jonathan score a penalty in Town's 3-0 FA Cup 3rd round home win during January 2009?

ALF RAMSEY

991.   In which year was Alf appointed as Ipswich Town manager after retiring from playing?

992.   Alf's first League game in charge of Ipswich, a 2-0 defeat at Portman Road, was against which team?

993.   To what position in the League did Alf guide Ipswich Town during his first season as manager?

994.   True or false: Alf guided Ipswich Town to the Division Three South title, winning on goal difference, during the 1956/57 season?

995.   Which League did Ipswich win under the management of Alf during the 1960/61 season?

996.   In what position did Alf play during his playing days?

997.   What was Alf's middle name – Ernest, Eric or Eli?

998.   How many of the 340 League games played under the management of Alf did Town win – 133, 163 or 193?

999.   Which Town manager did Alf take over from when he arrived at Portman Road?

1000.   Which team did Alf go on to manage when he left Portman Road in 1963?

ANSWERS

CLUB HISTORY

1.   1878

2.   True

3.   The Blues, Town and The Tractor Boys

4.   Bobby Robson

5.   FA Youth Cup

6.   Matteo Sereni

7.   Portsmouth

8.   True

9.   Once (1978)

10. 2007

ROY KEANE

11. Sunderland

12. April

13. Cardiff City (April 2009)

14. Manchester United

15. 15th

16. Maurice

17. Republic of Ireland

18. Nottingham Forest

19. 7

20. Grant Leadbitter

GEORGE BURLEY

21. Right back

22. Sunderland

23. True

24. Scotland

25. Dale Roberts

26. FA Cup winner (1978) and UEFA Cup winner (1981)

27.   1956

28.   Colchester United

29.   Leicester City

30.   7th

PLAYER OF THE YEAR - 1

31.   2009/10   Gareth McAuley

32.   2008/09   Richard Wright

33.   2007/08   Jonathan Walters

34.   2006/07   Sylvain Legwinski

35.   2005/06   Fabian Wilnis

36.   2004/05   Shefki Kuqi

37.   2003/04   Ian Westlake

38.   2002/03   Matt Holland

39.   2001/02   Mark Venus

40.   2000/01   Marcus Stewart

BOBBY ROBSON

41.   False: he never played for Ipswich Town

42.   20

43.   Texaco Cup (1973)

44.   England

45.   Bobby Ferguson

46.   2002

47.   6th

48.   1969

49.   Newcastle United

50.   PSV Eindhoven (1990-92 and 1998-99)

RAY CRAWFORD

51.   True

52.   *204*

53.   *Floriana*

54.   *Southampton*

55.   *3 (against Brighton & Hove Albion, Leeds United and Leyton Orient)*

56.   *Swansea*

57.   *Wolverhampton Wanderers and West Bromwich Albion*

58.   *2*

59.   *Curse of the Jungle Boy*

60.   *320*

FA CUP WINNERS – 1978

61.   *Wembley Stadium*

62.   *Arsenal*

63.   *Roger Osborne*

64.   *77th*

65.   *John Wark*

66.   *Mick Lambert*

67.   *Paul Cooper, George Burley, Mick Mills, Brian Talbot, Allan Hunter, Kevin Beattie, Roger Osborne, John Wark, Paul Mariner, David Geddis and Clive Woods*

68.   *Mick Mills*

69.   *West Bromwich Albion*

70.   *Millwall*

DIVISION ONE CHAMPIONS – 1961/1962

71.   *24*

72.   *Burnley*

73.   *Alf Ramsey*

74.   *Ray Crawford*

75.   *Ted Phillips*

76.   True: drawing 0-0 and then losing 4-3 and 4-2

77.   Aston Villa

78.   Chelsea

79.   22,863

80.   Roy Stephenson, Doug Moran, Ray Crawford (2), Ted Phillips
       and Jimmy Leadbetter

JASON DOZZELL

81.   1967

82.   16 years (and 56 days) old

83.   Crystal Palace

84.   False: but he did win nine Under-21 caps in his career

85.   53

86.   Tottenham Hotspur

87.   George Burley

88.   Colchester United

89.   Bobby Ferguson

90.   340: 320 (20)

TERRY BUTCHER

91.   3

92.   Everton

93.   2

94.   Bobby Robson

95.   False: he never managed Ipswich Town

96.   Defender (central)

97.   Ian

98.   FC Cologne

99.   Alan Brazil, John Wark and Paul Mariner

100.   Rangers

CLUB HONOURS

101.	Division One Champions	1962
102.	FA Cup Youth Winners	2005
103.	Texaco Cup Winners	1973
104.	Division One Runners-up	1981
105.	Division Two Champions	1992
106.	Division Three (South) Champions	1954
107.	Division Two Champions	1968
108.	Division Three (South) Champions	1957
109.	Division Two Champions	1961
110.	Division One Runners-up	1982

UEFA CUP WINNERS – 1981

111.	Aris Thessaloniki
112.	John Wark
113.	3-2 (3-0 at home and 0-2 away)
114.	Bobby Robson
115.	John Wark
116.	4-1
117.	Terry Butcher
118.	Frans Thijssen, John Wark and Paul Mariner
119.	AZ'67 Alkmaar
120.	5-4 (3-0 and 2-4)

NATIONALITIES – 1

121.	Alan Lee	Irish
122.	Jason de Vos	Canadian
123.	Matteo Sereni	Italian
124.	Martijn Reuser	Dutch
125.	Fabian Wilnis	Dutch
126.	Mich d'Avray	South African

107

127.	*Bontcho Guentchev*	*Bulgarian*
128.	*Mauricio Taricco*	*Argentinian*
129.	*David Johnson*	*Jamaican*
130.	*Gus Uhlenbeek*	*Dutch*

IPSWICH TOWN V. COLCHESTER UNITED

131. *Pablo Couñago and Kevin Lisbie*

132. *True*

133. *Division Three South*

134. *3-1 to Ipswich Town*

135. *Colchester (10th place; Ipswich 14th place)*

136. *David Wright*

137. *3-2 to Ipswich Town*

138. *True*

139. *The League Cup*

140. *4-0 to Ipswich Town*

LEGENDS – 1

141. *Mick Mills*

142. *Allan Hunter*

143. *Simon Milton*

144. *John Wark*

145. *Mick Stockwell*

146. *Russell Osman*

147. *Eric Gates*

148. *Paul Cooper*

149. *Tommy Parker*

150. *Colin Viljoen*

TOWN MANAGERS

| 151. | *Roy Keane* | *2009* |

152.	Jackie Milburn	1963
153.	George Burley	1994
154.	Bobby Robson	1969
155.	John Lyall	1990
156.	Alf Ramsey	1955
157.	Bobby Ferguson	1982
158.	Joe Royle	2002
159.	John Duncan	1987
160.	Jim Magilton	2006

UEFA CUP – 2002/2003

161.	Marcus Stewart
162.	8-1 to Ipswich Town
163.	Pablo Couñago
164.	FK Sartid Smederevo 1913
165.	1-1
166.	Darren Bent
167.	12
168.	Darren Bent
169.	Joe Royle
170.	Slovan Liberec

POSITIONS IN THE LEAGUE – 1

171.	1980/81	2nd in Division One
172.	1982/83	9th in Division One
173.	1984/85	17th in Division One
174.	1986/87	5th in Division Two
175.	1988/89	8th in Division Two
176.	1990/91	14th in Division Two
177.	1992/93	16th in Premier League
178.	1994/95	22nd in Premier League

179.	1996/97	4th in Division One
180.	1998/99	3rd in Division One

WHERE DID THEY GO? – 1

181.	Mick Stockwell	Colchester United
182.	David Johnson	Nottingham Forest
183.	Bobby Petta	Celtic
184.	Adam Tanner	Peterborough United
185.	Jason Cundy	Portsmouth
186.	Alex Mathie	Dundee United
187.	Danny Sonner	Sheffield Wednesday
188.	Claus Thomsen	Everton
189.	Steve Sedgley	Wolves
190.	Stuart Slater	Leicester City

TOWN IN THE LEAGUE CUP

191. Ray Crawford

192. Barnsley

193. False: Town were knocked out in the semi-finals by Liverpool, 4-2 on aggregate

194. Chelsea

195. Jamie Clapham and James Scowcroft

196. Colchester United

197. Paul Mariner

198. Tommy Miller and Ian Westlake

199. Trevor Whymark

200. Chris Kiwomya

BOBBY FERGUSON

201. Defender

202. 71

203.   **Brighton & Hove Albion**

204.   **True**

205.   **9th (1982/83)**

206.   **1938**

207.   **The club failed to win a penalty kick in 42 League matches**

208.   **True**

209.   **26**

210.   **False**

DIVISION ONE PLAY-OFF FINAL WINNERS – 2000

211.   **Barnsley**

212.   **4-2 to Ipswich**

213.   **Richard Wright**

214.   **Wembley Stadium**

215.   **Tony Mowbray**

216.   **Martijn Reuser**

217.   **George Burley**

218.   **Fabian Wilnis, Richard Naylor and Martijn Reuser**

219.   **Bolton Wanderers**

220.   **Jim Magilton**

ALAN BRAZIL

221.   **70**

222.   **Manchester United**

223.   **Sunderland**

224.   **13**

225.   **1959**

226.   **Tottenham Hotspur**

227.   **Southampton**

228.   **154: 143 (11)**

229.   **Striker**

230.   22

WHERE DID THEY COME FROM? – 1

231.	Grant Leadbitter	Sunderland
232.	Alex Bruce	Birmingham City
233.	Gareth McAuley	Leicester City
234.	Richard Wright	West Ham United
235.	Tamás Priskin	Watford
236.	Jonathan Walters	Chester City
237.	Neil Alexander	Cardiff City
238.	Lee Martin	Manchester United
239.	Iván Campo	Bolton Wanderers
240.	Jon Stead	Sheffield United

UEFA CUP – 2001/2002

241.   Titus Bramble

242.   Finidi George

243.   Marcus Stewart

244.   0-0

245.   Marcus Stewart

246.   True

247.   Alun Armstrong

248.   Feyenoord

249.   Alun Armstrong

250.   George Burley

TOWN IN THE FA CUP

251.   Tottenham Hotspur

252.   5th

253.   Mick Lambert

254.   Jack Colback and Owen Garvan

255.   *3-0 to Ipswich Town*

256.   *Richard Naylor, Tommy Miller and Shefki Kuqi*

257.   *Eric Gates*

258.   *Bradford City*

259.   *True*

260.   *West Ham United*

SQUAD NUMBERS – 2010/2011

261.	*Lee Martin*	*11*
262.	*Brian Murphy*	*1*
263.	*Alan Quinn*	*15*
264.	*David Norris*	*8*
265.	*Grant Leadbetter*	*6*
266.	*Jaime Peters*	*2*
267.	*Jonathan Stead*	*14*
268.	*Pablo Counago*	*18*
269.	*Carlos Edwards*	*7*
270.	*Connor Wickham*	*9*

POSITIONS IN THE LEAGUE – 2

271.	*1981/82*	*2nd in Division One*
272.	*1983/84*	*12th in Division One*
273.	*1985/86*	*20th in Division One*
274.	*1987/88*	*8th in Division Two*
275.	*1989/90*	*9th in Division Two*
276.	*1991/92*	*1st in Division Two*
277.	*1993/94*	*19th in Premier League*
278.	*1995/96*	*7th in Division One*
279.	*1997/98*	*5th in Division One*
280.	*1999/2000*	*3rd in Division One*

1960s

281.   *Andy Nelson*
282.   *Floriana*
283.   *True*
284.   *Colin Viljoen*
285.   *True*
286.   *Norwich City*
287.   *Joe Broadfoot*
288.   *John O'Rourke*
289.   *Crystal Palace*
290.   *121*

2009/2010

291.   *Derby County*
292.   *West Bromwich Albion*
293.   *Jon Stead*
294.   *15th*
295.   *David Healy*
296.   *Jon Stead*
297.   *Roy Keane*
298.   *Jonathan Walters*
299.   *Pablo Couñago*
300.   *Carlos Edwards*

KEVIN BEATTIE

301.   *24*
302.   *Bobby Robson*
303.   *Leeds United*
304.   *Mick Mills*
305.   *Sheffield United*
306.   *9*

307.   Central defender

308.   1980/81 (having started seven games during this season)

309.   228: 225 (3)

310.   Kevin is actually his middle name, his real name is Thomas

1970s

311.   Mick Mills

312.   True

313.   Allan Hunter

314.   Trevor Whymark

315.   Liverpool (1st) and Manchester City (2nd)

316.   Southampton

317.   Brian Talbot

318.   Leeds United

319.   Mick Hill and Rod Belfitt

320.   West Bromwich Albion

2008/2009

321.   9th

322.   Ben Thatcher

323.   Sheffield Wednesday

324.   12

325.   Richard Wright

326.   Kevin Lisbie

327.   Alan Quinn, Giovani dos Santos and Jon Stead

328.   Owen Garvan

329.   Iván Campo

330.   17

TED PHILLIPS

331.   1933

332. 5

333. Colchester United, Queens Park Rangers, Watford, Shrewsbury Town and Reading

334. 161

335. True

336. John

337. Leyton Orient

338. Scott Duncan

339. Swansea City

340. 269

BILL BAXTER

341. 409

342. Centre half

343. True

344. Northampton Town

345. 3

346. Alf Ramsey

347. Fulham

348. 21

349. 1939

350. Hull City

ERIC GATES

351. 73

352. Manchester City

353. True: 13 in 1983/84 and 13 in 1984/85

354. Bobby Robson

355. Barcelona

356. Striker

357. Sunderland

358. *True*

359. *Queens Park Rangers*

360. *1955 (28 June)*

ALLAN HUNTER

361. *Northern Ireland*

362. *280*

363. *Blackburn Rovers*

364. *1975/76*

365. *3*

366. *Bobby Robson*

367. *Arsenal*

368. *Colchester United*

369. *8*

370. *Centre back*

FRANK YALLOP

371. *True*

372. *Walter*

373. *Fullback*

374. *52*

375. *True*

376. *Everton*

377. *7*

378. *True: one goal away against Shrewsbury Town during September 1988 and one at home against Stoke City during January 1989*

379. *Tottenham Hotspur (in a 2-0 away win) and Manchester United (in a 2-1 home win) both during January 1993*

380. *316: 289 (27)*

STEVE McCALL

381.   7

382.   1960

383.   True

384.   Sheffield Wednesday

385.   New Zealand

386.   UEFA Cup winners' medal (1981)

387.   Harold

388.   False: Terry Butcher won the award this season

389.   Wolverhampton Wanderers

390.   257: 249 (8)

MICK MILLS

391.   591: 588 (3)

392.   Bill McGarry

393.   Dennis

394.   Bobby Robson

395.   22

396.   17 years (and 123 days) old

397.   1949

398.   True

399.   Wales

400.   42

PLAYER OF THE YEAR - 2

401.	1999/2000	James Scowcroft
402.	1998/99	Jamie Clapham
403.	1997/98	Matt Holland
404.	1996/97	Mauricio Taricco
405.	1995/96	Simon Milton
406.	1994/95	Craig Forrest

407.	1993/94	John Wark
408.	1992/93	Mick Stockwell
409.	1991/92	John Wark
410.	1990/91	David Linighan

RICHARD WRIGHT

411.	1977
412.	2
413.	True
414.	1
415.	Ian
416.	Arsenal
417.	Coventry City
418.	False: he didn't score any goals
419.	Everton
420.	Jim Magilton

SECOND DIVISION CHAMPIONS – 1991/1992

421.	Middlesbrough
422.	John Lyall
423.	Chris Kiwomya
424.	Steve Whitton (2) and Gavin Johnson
425.	Charlton Athletic
426.	24
427.	14,247
428.	Chris Kiwomya and Jason Dozzell
429.	False: 3 wins and 1 draw
430.	11

CAPPED TRACTOR BOYS – 1

| 431. | Arnold Mühren | 7 Dutch Caps |

432.	Eric Gates	2 English Caps
433.	Claus Thomsen	12 Danish Caps
434.	Matt Holland	33 Irish Caps
435.	Bryan Hamilton	21 Northern Irish Caps
436.	Frans Thijssen	10 Dutch Caps
437.	Craig Forrest	42 Canadian Caps
438.	John Wark	26 Scottish Caps
439.	Mick Mills	42 English Caps
440.	Frank Yallop	38 Canadian Caps

PORTMAN ROAD

441. Cobbold Stand

442. 9

443. Sir Alf Ramsey Way

444. Britannia Stand

445. IP1 2DA

446. 1884

447. Broom Hill and Brook's Hall

448. 450 yards

449. Croatia

450. Sir Alf Ramsey and Sir Bobby Robson

IPSWICH TOWN V. NORWICH CITY

451. True: 3-1 at home and 2-0 away

452. Jonathan Stead

453. 2-1 to Town

454. Alex Mathie

455. John Wark

456. 1962 (1961/62 season)

457. 4-1 to Town

458. True

459. *Norwich (4-2 at Portman Road)*

460. *Fabian Wilnis and Darren Bent*

1980s

461. *Terry Butcher*

462. *David Lowe*

463. *Bobby Robson, Bobby Ferguson and John Duncan*

464. *Nigel Gleghorn*

465. *True*

466. *39*

467. *Notts County*

468. *John Walk (13), Jason Dozzell (11), Dalian Atkinson (10) and Simon Milton (10)*

469. *Derby County*

470. *Kevin Wilson*

2007/2008

471. *Sheffield Wednesday*

472. *Jonathan Walters*

473. *Jim Magilton*

474. *8th*

475. *Alan Lee*

476. *Sheffield United*

477. *Jonathan Walters (13), Pablo Couñago (12) and Alan Lee (11)*

478. *Jason de Vos*

479. *Velice Sumulikoski*

480. *Pablo Couñago*

FRANS THIJSSEN

481. *10*

482. *Midfielder*

483. **Bobby Robson**

484. **Norwich City**

485. **125: 123 (2)**

486. **£200,000**

487. **1981**

488. **Bert Trautmann**

489. **Nottingham Forest**

490. **True: in the away leg, in a 4-2 defeat against AZ'67 Alkmaar**

ARNOLD MÜHREN

491. **5**

492. **Manchester United**

493. **UEFA Cup Winner (in 1981)**

494. **23**

495. **Chelsea**

496. **21**

497. **Liverpool**

498. **Midfielder**

499. **FC Twente**

500. **Bobby Robson**

PAUL MARINER

501. **Once (1982/83)**

502. **False: he never scored more than three goals in a competitive match**

503. **West Ham United**

504. **96**

505. **Plymouth Argyle**

506. **10**

507. **Bobby Robson**

508. **260**

509.   *True*

510.   *Manchester United*

MICK STOCKWELL

511.   *Coventry City*

512.   *True*

513.   *1992/93*

514.   *35*

515.   *FC Porto*

516.   *Derby County*

517.   *Thomas*

518.   *2000*

519.   *506: 464 (42)*

520.   *1965*

RICHARD NAYLOR

521.   *George Burley*

522.   *Portsmouth*

523.   *1977*

524.   *Millwall (August 2005) and Preston North End (March 2006)*

525.   *38*

526.   *2nd (after 52 minutes)*

527.   *4*

528.   *Alan*

529.   *2009*

530.   *Leeds United*

DARREN BENT

531.   *Charlton Athletic*

532.   *Middlesbrough*

533.   *12*

534. *Walsall*

535. *Sunderland*

536. *1984*

537. *Sunderland*

538. *47*

539. *Ashley*

540. *19*

MARTIJN REUSER

541. *1*

542. *Ajax*

543. *Fulham*

544. *6*

545. *Bradford City*

546. *14*

547. *Tommy Miller and Pablo Couñago*

548. *Franciscus*

549. *Midfielder*

550. *Gillingham*

FABIAN WILNIS

551. *De Graafschap*

552. *Swindon Town*

553. *George Burley*

554. *David Beckham*

555. *Darren Bent*

556. *Lloyd*

557. *Coventry City*

558. *1970*

559. *Colchester United*

560. *Grays Athletic*

2006/2007

561. 14th

562. Ipswich (Norwich City finished 16th)

563. Alan Lee

564. Barnsley

565. Jonathan Walters

566. Coventry City

567. Danny Haynes

568. True: 3 defeats and 1 draw

569. Shane Supple

570. Luton Town

CHRIS KIWOMYA

571. Bradford City

572. False: he never won any international caps in his football career

573. 225: 197 (28)

574. Walsall

575. Wigan Athletic

576. 51

577. Mark

578. Arsenal

579. True

580. John Duncan

SIMON MILTON

581. John Duncan

582. Midfielder

583. 1963

584. Bradford City

585. Bury Town

586. 48

587.   Charles

588.   Shrewsbury Town

589.   True

590.   281: 217 (64)

ROMEO ZONDERVAN

591.   True

592.   13

593.   West Bromwich Albion

594.   True: he won one international cap for Holland in his career

595.   1959

596.   Bobby Ferguson

597.   Watford

598.   True

599.   NAC Breda

600.   274: 270 (4)

JIM MAGILTON

601.   Sheffield Wednesday

602.   Liverpool

603.   True

604.   Joe Royle

605.   16

606.   1969

607.   True

608.   Leicester City

609.   Sheffield United

610.   Midfielder (central)

JOHN WARK

611.   135

612. *Escape to Victory*

613. *Young European Player of the Year and PFA Players' Player of the Year*

614. *True: 18 League, 2 FA Cup, 2 League Cup and 14 UEFA Cup goals*

615. *29*

616. *Liverpool*

617. *Wark On*

618. *20*

619. *3: 1974-83, 1987-89 and 1991-96*

620. *West Bromwich Albion*

KIERON DYER

621. *Newcastle United*

622. *1978*

623. *11*

624. *3 (1996/97, 1997/98 and 1998/99)*

625. *West Ham United*

626. *Sheffield United*

627. *Courtney*

628. *George Burley*

629. *True*

630. *Manchester City*

1990s

631. *Nottingham Forest*

632. *Claus Thomsen*

633. *Ian Marshall*

634. *Liverpool*

635. *Tony Mowbray*

636. *Leicester City*

637. *£1.20*

638. *Clive Baker*

639. *Tottenham Hotspur*

640. *Paul Goddard*

POT LUCK - 1

641. *True*

642. *Blue, white and red*

643. *Fisons*

644. *£3*

645. *True*

646. *Simon Clegg*

647. *Jackie Milburn, John Duncan, John Lyall, Joe Royle and Jim Magilton*

648. *2002 (2001/02 season)*

649. *12*

650. *Greene King*

2005/2006

651. *15th*

652. *Gavin Williams*

653. *Castro Sito*

654. *Jimmy Juan*

655. *5*

656. *Lewis Price and Shane Supple*

657. *Cardiff City*

658. *Alan Lee*

659. *Joe Royle*

660. *Nicky Forster*

RUSSELL OSMAN

661. *Charles*

662. *Central defender*

663. *True*

664. *Tottenham Hotspur*

665. *1959*

666. *Leicester City*

667. *17*

668. *Chelsea*

669. *Cardiff City*

670. *294*

PAUL COOPER

671. *447*

672. *Goalkeeper*

673. *David*

674. *Birmingham City*

675. *19*

676. *Stockport County*

677. *FA Cup (in 1978) and UEFA Cup (in 1981)*

678. *1953*

679. *False: he did not win any international honours during his career*

680. *Leicester City*

CLIVE WOODS

681. *Winger*

682. *Newcastle United*

683. *267: 217 (50)*

684. *Everton*

685. *1947*

686. *True*

687. *West Ham United*

688.   24

689.   Richard

690.   Norwich City

BRYAN HAMILTON

691.   153: 142 (11)

692.   Coventry City

693.   Bobby Robson

694.   Trevor Whymark

695.   Manchester United

696.   True

697.   Northern Ireland

698.   Newcastle United

699.   Everton

700.   43

JOHN LYALL

701.   1990

702.   Clive Baker

703.   West Ham United

704.   1940

705.   16

706.   False: he never managed England

707.   Defender

708.   True (1991/92 season)

709.   61

710.   Angus

WHERE DID THEY COME FROM? – 2

711.   Darren Currie   Brighton & Hove Albion

712.   Jason de Vos   Wigan Athletic

713.	Georges Santos	Grimsby Town
714.	Neill Rimmer	Everton
715.	Steve Whitton	Sheffield Wednesday
716.	Jamie Clapham	Tottenham Hotspur
717.	John McGreal	Tranmere Rovers
718.	Eddie Youds	Everton
719.	Andy Marshall	Norwich City
720.	Marcus Bent	Blackburn Rovers

LEGENDS – 2

721.	Bill Baxter
722.	Doug Rees
723.	Jason Dozzell
724.	Frank Yallop
725.	Roy Bailey
726.	Jimmy Leadbetter
727.	John Elsworthy
728.	George Burley
729.	Matt Holland
730.	Jim Magilton

POSITIONS IN THE LEAGUE – 3

731.	1961/62	1st in Division One
732.	1963/64	22nd in Division One
733.	1965/66	15th in Division Two
734.	1967/68	1st in Division Two
735.	1969/70	18th in Division One
736.	1971/72	13th in Division One
737.	1973/74	4th in Division One
738.	1975/76	6th in Division One
739.	1977/78	18th in Division One

| 740. | 1979/80 | 3rd in Division One |

2004/2005

741.	Gillingham
742.	Sheffield United
743.	Tommy Miller
744.	West Ham United
745.	Joe Royle
746.	Kevin Horlock
747.	Ian Westlake
748.	Darren Bent and Shefki Kuqi
749.	3rd
750.	Darren Currie

1992/1993 – FIRST PREMIER LEAGUE SEASON

751.	16th
752.	Aston Villa
753.	Gavin Johnson
754.	John Lyall
755.	True: won 2 and drew 6
756.	David Linighan
757.	Bontcho Guentchev
758.	12
759.	Jason Dozzell
760.	10

ROGER OSBORNE

761.	9
762.	False: he never won this award while at Portman Road
763.	Midfielder
764.	Birmingham City

765.   *Colchester United*

766.   *He had a knee injury*

767.   *124: 109 (15)*

768.   *1950*

769.   *Wolverhampton Wanderers*

770.   *Bobby Robson*

TREVOR WHYMARK

771.   *West Bromwich Albion*

772.   *14*

773.   *John*

774.   *75*

775.   *Norwich City*

776.   *Lazio*

777.   *Bobby Robson (during the 1969/70 season)*

778.   *Forward*

779.   *261: 249 (12)*

780.   *14*

COLIN VILJOEN

781.   *Norwich City*

782.   *True*

783.   *305: 303 (2)*

784.   *6*

785.   *Portsmouth*

786.   *Manchester United*

787.   *Midfielder*

788.   *Manchester City*

789.   *South Africa (Johannesburg)*

790.   *45*

ROY STEPHENSON

791.   *Alf Ramsey*
792.   *21*
793.   *Southampton*
794.   *Leicester*
795.   *1965*
796.   *Brighton & Hove Albion*
797.   *144*
798.   *9*
799.   *True*
800.   *1932*

PLAYER OF THE YEAR - 3

801.	1989/90	John Wark
802.	1988/89	John Wark
803.	1987/88	Frank Yallop
804.	1986/87	Romeo Zondervan
805.	1985/86	Terry Butcher
806.	1984/85	Terry Butcher
807.	1983/84	Trevor Putney
808.	1982/83	Paul Mariner
809.	1981/82	Alan Brazil
810.	1980/81	Paul Cooper

PABLO COUÑAGO

811.   *9*
812.   *Malaga*
813.   *Spanish*
814.   *17*
815.   *Rotherham United*
816.   *1979*

817. *Celta Vigo*

818. *True*

819. *Striker*

820. *Swansea City*

MATT HOLLAND

821. *5*

822. *Bournemouth*

823. *1974*

824. *38*

825. *George Burley*

826. *Midfielder (central)*

827. *Bolton Wanderers*

828. *Stoke City*

829. *Rhys*

830. *10*

JOE ROYLE

831. *74*

832. *2002*

833. *Striker*

834. *5th (2003/04)*

835. *Watford (December 2002)*

836. *1949*

837. *Tony Mowbray*

838. *Everton and Manchester City*

839. *Twice (2004 and 2005, losing to West Ham United on both occasions)*

840. *2005/06*

NATIONALITIES – 2

841.	Frans Thijssen	Dutch
842.	Alan Brazil	Scottish
843.	Gerard Baker	American
844.	Gareth McAuley	Northern Irish
845.	Giovani dos Santos	Mexican
846.	Reggie Lambe	Bermudian
847.	Finidi George	Nigerian
848.	Shefki Kuqi	Finnish
849.	Gavin Williams	Welsh
850.	Jaime Peters	Canadian

CAPPED TRACTOR BOYS – 2

851.	Kevin Beattie	9 English Caps
852.	Richard Wright	1 English Cap
853.	Alan Brazil	11 Scottish Caps
854.	Gavin Williams	1 Welsh Cap
855.	Jason de Vos	6 Canadian Caps
856.	Bontcho Guentchev	7 Bulgarian Caps
857.	Hermann Hreidarsson	16 Icelandic Caps
858.	Shefki Kuqi	7 Finnish Caps
859.	David Johnson	4 Jamaican Caps
860.	Finidi George	7 Nigerian Caps

WHERE DID THEY GO? – 2

861.	Dean Bowditch	Yeovil Town
862.	Richard Naylor	Leeds United
863.	Alan Lee	Crystal Palace
864.	Darren Ambrose	Newcastle United
865.	Kelvin Davis	Sunderland
866.	Alun Armstrong	Darlington

867.	Kevin Horlock	Doncaster Rovers
868.	Gavin Williams	Bristol City
869.	Neil Alexander	Rangers
870.	Lewis Price	Derby County

POT LUCK – 2

871. Alf Ramsey (with nearly 48% of matches being Town League victories)

872. Tommy Smith

873. Wales

874. Luciano Civelli

875. Brian Murphy

876. False: all Town managers have been English, Scottish or Irish

877. 1981

878. The Uhrencup

879. Red

880. Doncaster Rovers

2000/2001

881. 5th

882. Richard Wright (36 games) and Keith Branagan

883. Matt Holland

884. 19

885. Hermann Hreidarsson

886. Marcus Stewart

887. 3-0 to Ipswich

888. Titus Bramble

889. George Burley

890. 20

JOHN ELSWORTHY

891. False

892. Notts County

893. 398

894. True

895. Coventry City

896. Scott Duncan

897. Newport County

898. Floriana (in a 10-0 win)

899. 44

900. Wing half

JIMMY LEADBETTER

901. 1928

902. Brighton & Hove Albion

903. 344

904. Mansfield Town

905. 13

906. Bournemouth

907. False: he played as an outside left

908. Alf Ramsey

909. 43

910. Sudbury Town

BRIAN TALBOT

911. Burnley

912. Midfielder

913. Bobby Robson

914. 177

915. Luton Town

916. Arsenal

917. *Ernest*

918. *Northern Ireland*

919. *25*

920. *1953*

DAVID LINIGHAN

921. *West Ham United*

922. *38*

923. *True: 1990/91, 1991/92, 1992/93, 1993/94 and 1994/95*

924. *12*

925. *Blackpool*

926. *Shrewsbury Town*

927. *277: 275 (2)*

928. *Leicester City*

929. *John Duncan*

930. *True*

JAMES SCOWCROFT

931. *1975*

932. *George Burley*

933. *2*

934. *Wolverhampton Wanderers*

935. *Crewe Alexandra*

936. *David Johnson*

937. *1999/2000*

938. *Leicester City*

939. *47*

940. *2005*

TOMMY MILLER

941. *2*

942.	William
943.	Crewe Alexandra
944.	Scotland
945.	Hartlepool United
946.	Nottingham Forest
947.	Millwall
948.	1979
949.	Sheffield Wednesday
950.	6

ALAN LEE

951.	Cardiff City
952.	Sheffield United
953.	16
954.	Luton Town
955.	Republic of Ireland
956.	Crystal Palace
957.	Sheffield Wednesday
958.	Meggs
959.	Southampton
960.	Joe Royle

GERAINT WILLIAMS

961.	George
962.	13
963.	1992
964.	Leeds United
965.	2
966.	John Lyall
967.	Aston Villa
968.	217

969. Colchester United

970. 37

2001/2002

971. Southampton

972. 5-0 to Ipswich

973. Blackburn Rovers

974. Tottenham Hotspur

975. George Burley

976. 18th

977. 9

978. Matt Holland and Hermann Hreidarsson

979. Finidi George

980. Marcus Bent

JONATHAN WALTERS

981. 19

982. Chester City

983. Jim Magilton

984. Cardiff City

985. 13

986. Bristol City

987. 1983

988. Stoke City

989. Queens Park Rangers

990. Chesterfield

ALF RAMSEY

991. 1955

992. Torquay United (during August 1955)

993. 3rd (in Division Three South, during 1955/56)

994. *True*

995. *Division Two*

996. *Right back*

997. *Ernest*

998. *163*

999. *Scott Duncan*

1000. *England*

NOTES:

NOTES:

NOTES:

NOTES:

NOTES:

OTHER BOOKS BY CHRIS COWLIN:

* Celebrities' Favourite Football Teams

* The British TV Sitcom Quiz Book

* The Cricket Quiz Book

* The Gooners Quiz Book

* The Horror Film Quiz Book

* The Official Aston Villa Quiz Book

* The Official Birmingham City Quiz Book

* The Official Brentford Quiz Book

* The Official Bristol Rovers Quiz Book

* The Official Burnley Quiz Book

* The Official Bury Quiz Book

* The Official Carlisle United Quiz Book

* The Official Carry On Quiz Book

* The Official Chesterfield Football Club Quiz Book

* The Official Colchester United Quiz Book

* The Official Coventry City Quiz Book

* The Official Doncaster Rovers Quiz Book

* The Official Greenock Morton Quiz Book

* The Official Heart of Midlothian Quiz Book

* The Official Hereford United Quiz Book

* The Official Hull City Quiz Book

* The Official Ipswich Town Quiz Book

OTHER BOOKS BY CHRIS COWLIN:

* The Official Leicester City Quiz Book

* The Official Macclesfield Town Quiz Book

* The Official Norwich City Football Club Quiz

* The Official Notts County Quiz Book

* The Official Peterborough United Quiz Book

* The Official Port Vale Quiz Book

* The Official Queen of the South Quiz Book

* The Official Rochdale AFC Quiz Book

* The Official Rotherham United Quiz Book

* The Official Sheffield United Quiz Book

* The Official Shrewsbury Town Quiz Book

* The Official Stockport County Quiz Book

* The Official Walsall Football Club Quiz Book

* The Official Watford Football Club Quiz Book

* The Official West Bromwich Albion Quiz Book

* The Official Wolves Quiz Book

* The Official Yeovil Town Quiz Book

* The Reality Television Quiz Book

* The Southend United Quiz Book

* The Spurs Quiz Book

* The Sunderland AFC Quiz Book

* The Ultimate Derby County Quiz Book

* The West Ham United Quiz Book

www.apexpublishing.co.uk